Math Logic & Word Problems

3-4

Written by
Angela Higgs

Editors: Carla Hamaguchi and Collene Dobelmann
Illustrator: Corbin Hillam
Designer/Production: Moonhee Pak/Cari Helstrom
Cover Designer: Barbara Peterson
Art Director: Tom Cochrane
Project Director: Carolea Williams

Reprinted 2008

Table of Contents

Introduction

Each book in the *Power Practice*™ series contains over 100 ready-to-use activity pages to provide students with skill practice. The fun activities can be used to supplement and enhance what you are already teaching in your classroom. Give an activity page to students as independent class work, or send the pages home as homework to reinforce skills taught in class. An answer key is provided for quick reference.

Math Logic & Word Problems 3–4 provides activities that will directly assist students in practicing and solving logic and problem-solving challenges, as well as reinforcing math skills such as decimals, fractions, addition, subtraction, multiplication, division, graphing, time, and probability. The book is organized by the National Council of Teachers of Mathematics (NCTM) standards and contains motivating activities that cover number and operations, algebra, geometry, measurement, and data analysis and probability.

The activities include various types of logic questions. The activities are grouped in "sets" that cover each type of question. The first activity page of each set includes a brief explanation of which strategies to use to complete the problem. These pages include a section called "Strategic Steps" that explain how to solve the problem. The subhead "Show Me the Way" identifies these pages. The remaining pages offer students a chance to independently practice using the strategies and steps to solve similar problems.

Use these ready-to-go activities to "recharge" skill review and give students the power to succeed!

Backyard Leaves

Show Me the Way

> As the end of fall arrives, one Saturday evening you count all the leaves on the tree in your backyard.
>
> Here are clues to what happened the week before:
> - On Sunday ½ of the leaves fall off the tree.
> - On Monday ½ of the remaining leaves fall off the tree.
> - On Tuesday 20 leaves fall off the tree.
> - On Tuesday evening there were 10 leaves left on the tree.
>
> How many leaves were on the tree on Saturday? _____

Strategic Steps

The only information you know is the number of leaves on the tree on Tuesday evening, so you will work backward from there to find out how many were on the tree on Saturday.

1 On Tuesday evening there were 10 leaves on the tree. You know that 20 leaves fell off on Tuesday. Add those together, and you'll know how many were on the tree Monday evening.

$$10 + 20 = \underline{30} \text{ (leaves on Monday evening)}$$

2 You know that on Monday ½ of the leaves on the tree fell off (the number you determined in step 1). You will then multiply that number by 2 to find how many leaves were on the tree Monday morning.

$$\underline{36} \text{ (leaves on Monday evening)} \times 2 = \underline{60} \text{ (leaves on Sunday evening)}$$

3 You know that on Sunday ½ of the leaves on the tree fell off, so once again, you will multiply your answer by 2.

$$\underline{60} \text{ (leaves on Sunday evening)} \times 2 = \underline{120} \text{ (leaves on Saturday evening)}$$

Math Logic & Word Problems • 3–4 © 2005 Creative Teaching Press

Yummy Muffins

Read about the people who came to Mr. Lang's bakery. Then solve the problems.

- Mr. Lang makes the best muffins in town! This morning he put out trays of muffins.
- Mrs. Santos was the first customer. She bought a dozen muffins.
- Miss Gardner came in next. She bought half of the muffins that were left.
- Mr. Biggs was the third customer. He bought half the muffins that were left.
- Mrs. Kim arrived next. She bought eight muffins.
- After Mrs. Kim left, there were only four muffins left on the tray.

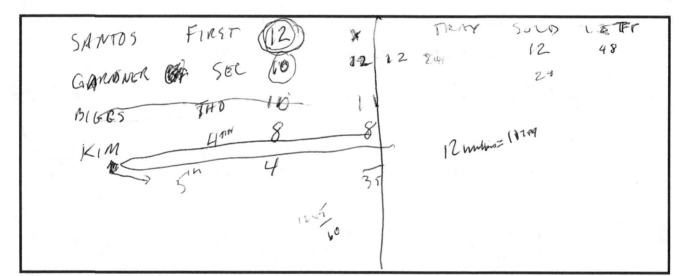

How many muffins did each of the customers buy?   FIGURE 12 muffins in each tray

Mrs. Kim _____ 8 _____   Mr. Biggs _____ 12 _____

Miss Gardner _____ 24 _____   Mrs. Santos _____ 12 _____

How many muffins did Mr. Lang put out that morning? _____ 60 _____

Math Logic & Word Problems • 3–4 © 2005 Creative Teaching Press

Library Sale

The Friends of City Public Library were having a book sale. The first five customers were Nathaniel, Nellie, Delia, Edmund, and Allison.

- Nathaniel was the first customer. He bought ½ as many books as Nellie.
- Nellie came in second. She bought twice as many books as Delia.
- Delia was the third customer. She bought the same number of books as Edmund.
- Edmund was the fourth customer. He bought twice as many books as Allison.
- Allison was the fifth customer. She bought 20 books.

> NATHANEL   FIRST   40
> NELLIE   2ND   DELIA   80 Books
> 3rd   40 Books
> DELIA
>
> EDMUND   4th   40 BOOKS
> ALLISON   5th   20 Books

How many books did each friend buy?

Nathaniel ____40____   Nellie ____80____

Delia ____40____   Edmund ____40____

Allison ____20____

How many books did the five friends buy altogether? ____220____

Strawberry Field

SHOW ME THE WAY

Jessica, Kate, and Brenna were planting strawberries when it started to rain. Inside, they were trying to find out how many plants each of the girls planted.

- Jessica planted 2 fewer strawberry plants than Brenna.
- Kate planted 3 more strawberry plants than Brenna.
- Brenna planted ¼ of the strawberry plants they had bought.
- The box contained 24 strawberry plants.

How many strawberry plants did each girl plant?

Jessica _____   Kate _____   Brenna _____

How many strawberry plants did they have left? _____

Strategic Steps   (Note: This is only one strategy. There are other ways to solve this problem.)

1. There are 24 strawberry plants in the box. Draw a box with 24 sections on a piece of graph paper.

2. From your diagram, you can see that half of 24 will be 12. Now divide one-half of your box in half again, giving you 2 sections that each show one-fourth of the box.

3. You can now count and see that there are 6 plants in one-fourth of the box. This is the number of plants that Brenna planted.

4. The other two are simple addition or subtraction sentences to write and solve.

    Jessica: 6 – 2 = _____   Kate: 6 + 3 = _____

5. To find the number of strawberry plants left, you would add up all the plants that the three girls planted and then subtract that total from the starting number of 24.

    _____ + _____ + _____ = _____   24 – _____ = _____

Math Logic & Word Problems • 3–4 © 2005 Creative Teaching Press

Reading Contest

Margaret, Betty, Chalondra, and Pete all entered the class reading contest. Together they read 64 pages.

- Pete read ¼ of the total pages.
- Betty read 4 fewer pages than Chalondra.
- Margaret read 4 more pages than Pete.
- Chalondra read 4 fewer pages than Margaret.

64
P 16
M
B
C

How many pages did each student read?

Pete _____ 16

Betty _____ 12

Chalondra _____ 16

Margaret _____ 20

4   64

PETE = = 4 · $\frac{f}{4}$ 16

B = = c-

Name _____ Date _____

Runs

Tim, Decker, Dean, and Cody are all on the same baseball team. They are trying to find out how many runs each of the boys scored.

- The four boys scored a total of 36 runs this season.
- Cody scored ⅓ of those runs.
- Decker scored 2 fewer runs than Cody.
- Dean scored 2 more runs than Tim.
- Dean scored 2 fewer runs than Decker.

How many runs did each boy score?

Tim _____   Decker _____

Cody _____   Dean _____

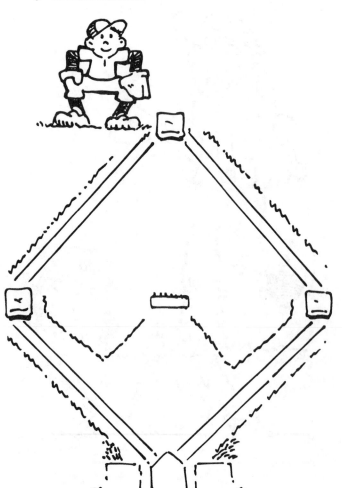

Math Logic & Word Problems • 3–4 © 2005 Creative Teaching Press

What Operation?

SHOW ME THE WAY

One-Step Problems
Fill in the operation sign and equals sign. Some will be in the format 1 + 2 = 3, and some will be 3 = 1 + 2. Find the method that gives you a correct answer.

6 ___ 7 ___ 13

Strategic Steps

1 For each problem, find the largest number, and then look at the relationship between the two smaller numbers and the largest number.   6 ___ 7 ___ 13 In this number sentence, the largest number is 13.

2 Ask yourself these questions: *Do you add the numbers together or subtract them? Do you multiply? Do you divide the larger number by one of the smaller numbers?* Once you decide on the operation, fill in the operation sign and equals sign.

3 In this case, there is only one possible solution: adding 6 and 7 to equal 13. Fill in the addition sign and equals sign.   6 ___ 7 ___ 13

Two-Step Problems
Use ( ) to show the first step you do as you are filling in the operation sign and equals sign.

Example: 1 ___ 2 ___ 3 ___ 9   This could be (1 + 2) × 3 = 9

2 ___ 4 ___ 6 ___ 36

Strategic Step

1 Use the information from solving a one-step problem and look for relationships between the numbers. Look at the first set of numbers. Take the largest number and divide that by the 6. The answer is 6. Likewise, if you add the 2 and 4, the answer is 6. Multiply this result by the 6, and you get the 36. Fill in the parentheses, addition sign, multiplication sign, and equals sign.

2 ___ 4 ___ 6 ___ 36

What Will You Do?

For the following one-step problems, fill in the operation sign and equals sign. Some will be in the format 1 + 2 = 3, and some will be 3 = 1 + 2. Find the method that gives you a correct answer.

A. 8 _____ 4 _____ 32

B. 42 _____ 7 _____ 6

C. 63 _____ 7 _____ 9

D. 32 _____ 21 _____ 11

E. 6 _____ 4 _____ 24

F. 48 _____ 42 _____ 6

For the following two-step problems, use ( ) to show the first step you do as you are filling in the operation sign and equals sign.

Example: 1 ___ 2 ___ 3 ___ 9
This could be: (1 + 2) × 3 = 9.

G. 24 _____ 14 _____ 18 _____ 28

H. 3 _____ 7 _____ 6 _____ 15

I. 9 _____ 7 _____ 12 _____ 24

J. 8 _____ 3 _____ 4 _____ 20

K. 8 _____ 3 _____ 3 _____ 33

L. 36 _____ 4 _____ 2 _____ 18

M. 4 _____ 5 _____ 2 _____ 40

N. 9 _____ 3 _____ 3 _____ 18

Math Logic & Word Problems • 3–4 © 2005 Creative Teaching Press

 **What Do You Pick?**

A. Gabrielle set up a stand to sell the honey she collected from her bees. She started the day with 18 jars of honey. At lunch she had 7 jars. How many jars of honey did Gabrielle sell by lunch? What operation will you use? Write a number sentence to show how you solve the problem.

B. Rashid and his friend Tiffany collect baseball cards. They traded some cards. Rashid started with 19 cards, and now, he has 26 cards. Did Rashid gain or lose cards? What operation will you use? Write a number sentence to show how you solve the problem.

C. Mr. Cook bought 48 cupcakes for the scout meeting. There are 24 children in the troop. How many cupcakes will each child get? What operation will you use? Write a number sentence to show how you solve the problem.

D. Gabe and his father picked twelve bushels of corn. Each bushel had four dozen ears of corn. They sold the corn for $5 per dozen. How much money did they make? Will you use more than one step? What operation or operations will you use? Write a number sentence(s) to show how you solve the problem.

Place-Value Riddles

SHOW ME THE WAY

A.   305   3005   35   3050   3500

1. I am greater than 300.
2. I have a 5 in the ones place.
3. I have a 0 in the hundreds place.
4. Who am I?

Strategic Steps

1 The first clue is that the number is greater than 300. You can eliminate the one number that is less than that. Cross out the number that is less than 300.

2 The second clue states that there is a 5 in the ones place. You can now eliminate the two numbers that do not have a 5 in the ones place. Now you are down to just two possible choices.

3 This clue says that there is a 0 in the hundreds place. There is only one choice left with that possibility. Circle that number.

Now try these two riddles.

B.   432   4023   4032   4302   40302

1. I am greater than 4,000.
2. I have a 2 in the ones place.
3. I have a 0 in the hundreds place.
4. Who am I?

C.   56808   68   5068   50608   5680

1. I am greater than 500.
2. I have an 8 in the ones place.
3. I have a 6 in the tens place.
4. Who am I?

Math Logic & Word Problems • 3–4 © 2005 Creative Teaching Press

Where Do I Go?

Takeshi dropped the place-value chart that Mr. Ballard spent a lot of time preparing. All the information is there, but the numbers are all in a jumble on the floor. Help Takeshi put the right numbers in the right places.

A. This four-digit number has a 2 in the tens place, a 4 in the hundreds place, and a 3 in the thousands place. The 0 stayed in the ones place. What is the number?

B. This number has four places and two 0s. The 8 goes in the thousands place, and another 8 goes in the ones place. All other places have 0s. What is the number?

C. In this four-digit number, there is a 3 in the ones place, a 5 in the tens place, an 8 in the thousands place, and a 1 in the hundreds place. What is the number?

D. The numbers left on the floor are 4, 3, 9, 7, and a second 4. Takeshi went to Mr. Ballard for help. Mr. Ballard said, "One 4 goes in the hundreds place, and the other 4 does not go next to it. The ones place has the smallest number. The 9 is to the left of the 7." What is the number?

 # Riddle Contest

Miss Woo's class was given an assignment to write problems to challenge other students to solve a place-value mystery. The following problems are the winners of this challenge. Solve the riddles.

A. Julianna's problem: I have six places in my number. The number 2 appears twice next to each other. The number 4 comes at the end. The number 8 is first in line. The numbers 5 and 6 are fighting and are separated by the 2s. The 5 is farther left than the 6. What number am I?

B. Anika's problem: I have seven places. I end with a 0, and I start with a 4. The number 5 is exactly in the middle. To the left of the 5 is a 3, and to the right of the 5 is a 6. I have a 7 in the tens place. The second digit is one less than 3. What number am I?

C. Patrick's problem: I am a small number with only three places. The numbers include 4, 9, and 3. I am not divisible by 2. The numbers in the tens and ones places add up to 7. What number am I?

D. Kai's problem: I have four places. I am divisible by 5, but I do not end with a 0. My hundreds place has nothing, but does have a number. My tens place has a 3. The digits in my hundreds and thousands places added together equal 8. What number am I?

E. Now it's your turn. Write your own place-value riddle to share with a friend.

Math Logic & Word Problems • 3–4 © 2005 Creative Teaching Press

What Do I Need?

SHOW ME THE WAY

> Some problems have more information than you need, and some do not have enough information to solve the problem. You have to read carefully to know what the question is asking and what information you need.
>
> **A.** In the forest, eight squirrels collected acorns from nine trees. They collected 25 acorns from each tree. How many acorns did the squirrels collect?
>
> _____

Strategic Steps

1 What is the question asking? Once that is determined, it's a simple problem. The question is asking how many acorns the squirrels collected. We know that they collected 25 acorns from a total of nine trees. Do we need to know how many squirrels actually collected the acorns?

2 Once you know what the problem is asking, ignore the information that is not needed, and solve the problem. In this case, you would need to multiply the number of acorns collected from each tree by the number of trees.

$25 \times 9 =$ _____

> **B.** Brady bought two sets of trading cards for $6.99 each. He also bought a carton of milk for $0.39 and an apple for $0.45. How much money did he have left?

Strategic Steps

1 What is the question asking? You know how much money Brady spent by adding up the amounts in the problem. How do you determine how much he has left? You cannot. To find that out, you must first know the amount of money he started with.

2 The answer to this problem is "not enough information."

Too Much or Too Little?

Some problems have more information than you need, and some do not have enough information to solve the problem. You have to read carefully to know what the question is asking and what information you need. Solve each problem.

A. Soo Jin has $8.65. She wants to buy a movie ticket for $5.00, a soda for $1.75, and a box of popcorn. Does she have enough money?

B. Emily bought 48 ears of corn, 36 tomatoes, and 24 fresh peaches from a farmer's market for her picnic. All the corn was eaten. If five people ate 3 peaches each, how many peaches were eaten?

C. Martina made sandwiches for her parents, her brothers, and three friends. How many sandwiches did she make?

D. A recipe calls for ¼ cup of brown sugar, ¼ cup of honey, 2 egg whites, ¾ cup of flour, and 1 cup of milk. How many cups of dry ingredients does the recipe require?

E. Every day for a week, Elizabeth walked 2 miles. After her walk, she stopped and bought an apple for $0.25 and a bottle of water for $0.80 at a stand in the park. How much did she spend at the park stand each week?

Math Logic & Word Problems • 3–4 © 2005 Creative Teaching Press

What Do I Really Need?

Some problems have more information than you need, and some do not have enough information to solve the problem. You have to read carefully to know what the question is asking and what information you need. For each question, state if you have too much information, not enough information, or just the right information to solve the problem. If possible, solve the problems.

A. Sylvie leaves at 7:15 every morning. School is over at 3:15 p.m. She then has band practice for an hour. It takes her 15 minutes to walk home. What time does she get home every afternoon?

B. Cody was trying to find the area of the board he was using for his science project. The length is 16 inches, the width is 10 inches, and the height is 1 inch. What is the area?

C. Jayson rode his bike 125 miles in a week. If he rode 28 miles on Monday, how far did he ride on Tuesday and on Wednesday?

D. A store manager ordered four cases of candy treats for Halloween. There are six bags of candy in each box and twelve boxes in a case. How many bags of candy did he order?

E. At the beginning of track season, Chelsea ran the mile in 7 minutes, 42 seconds. Christina ran the mile in 6 minutes, 22 seconds. Gwen ran the mile in 6 minutes, 45 seconds. At the end of track season, all three girls could run the mile in 6 minutes, 22 seconds. What is the difference in the time from the beginning of track season to the end of track season for Chelsea?

Math Logic & Word Problems • 3–4 © 2005 Creative Teaching Press

Name _____ Date _____

Fractions

SHOW ME THE WAY

A. How much is ½ of 6? _____

Strategic Step

❶ Look at the diagram of six ducks. To solve this problem, divide six ducks into two groups.

B. Elias had two equal squares of clay. He divided one square into two parts, and he gave one part to Kyle. He divided the other square into four parts, and he gave two parts to Kendall. Did Kyle or Kendall have more clay? _____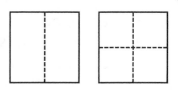

Strategic Step

❶ Color one section of the first square on the diagram. Then color two sections of the second square. Compare the sizes. Don't forget that "same size" is also a choice.

C. Caitlyn had four glasses of water. Help her arrange them in order from least to greatest volume.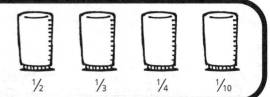

Strategic Step

❶ Each glass has been divided into sections. Using the fraction below the glass, color in that much water. Look at the glasses, and then arrange them from least to greatest volume.

Math Logic & Word Problems • 3–4 © 2005 Creative Teaching Press

What Part?

A. How much is ⅕ of 10?

B. Lauren had two large cookies. She cut one into three equal parts and gave one part to Phillip. Then she cut the other cookie into six equal parts and gave two parts to Tiffany. Who received more cookie, Tiffany or Phillip?

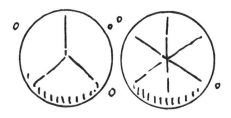

C. Madison is helping out at her mother's stationery shop. Her mother asked her to put the opened packs of paper in order from greatest to least amount of paper. In what order did Madison arrange the packs of paper?

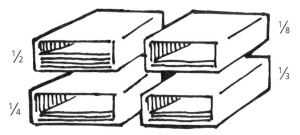

D. Julie had ⅓ cup of apple juice and mixed it with ⅓ cup of water. How much drink did she have?

Math Logic & Word Problems • 3–4 © 2005 Creative Teaching Press

Who Has More?

A. How much is ¼ of 12?

B. Gretchen had two packages of chocolate fudge. She cut one package into four equal pieces and gave Paul one piece. She cut the other package into eight equal pieces and gave Brad three pieces. Who had more fudge, Paul or Brad?

C. Neal was helping his mother clean out the refrigerator. They found four bottles of ketchup, all partly used. Neal's mother asked him to put the bottles in order from the one with the least amount of ketchup to the one with the greatest amount so they could be used up. In what order did Neal arrange the bottles of ketchup?

⅔   ¼   ½   ⅛

D. A pizza was cut into eight slices. During the movie, the Styles family ate three-eighths of the pizza. After the movie, Eric ate one-fourth of the pizza while putting it away. How much of the pizza was eaten?

Math Logic & Word Problems • 3–4 © 2005 Creative Teaching Press

How Many Steps?

SHOW ME THE WAY

A. Roman has four boxes. In each box, there are 16 cookies. Roman wants to use all his cookies and put an equal number on each of eight plates. How many cookies will he put on each plate?

Strategic Steps

1 This problem has two steps. First, you need to find out the total number of cookies. To do this, you will multiply the number of cookies in a box by the number of boxes.

16 (cookies) $\times$ 4 (boxes) = _____ (total cookies)

2 Now you want to know how many cookies to put on each plate. To do this, you will divide the total number of cookies you found in the first step by the number of plates.

_____ (total cookies) $\div$ 8 (plates) = _____ (number of cookies per plate)

B. Lydia divided her baseball cards into teams. There are eight teams that have 17 cards. There are seven teams that have 18 cards. How many cards are there altogether?

Strategic Steps

1 First, you would multiply the number of teams times the number of cards.

8 × 17 = _____   7 × 18 = _____

2 You would then add those two numbers together. Write and solve a number sentence to show this.

More Than One Step

A. Mariah and her family went to the movies. Her parents and grandmother needed adult tickets that cost $5.50 each. Mariah and her four siblings needed children's tickets that cost $4.00 each. How much did the tickets cost altogether?

B. There were 65 boxes shipped to the warehouse. In each box, there were 20 cartons. In each carton, there were 50 balloons. How many balloons were there altogether?

C. There are 30 cartons of bouncy balls. Each carton has 144 balls. The cartons are going to be loaded in a truck; however, each truck can only hold 15 cartons. How many trucks are needed? How many balls will there be in each truck?

D. Carter bought nine pizzas. Each pizza had eight slices. Carter wants to divide the pizza slices evenly among 24 people. How many slices will each person get?

Math Logic & Word Problems • 3–4 © 2005 Creative Teaching Press

First This, Then That

A. Malik was at a yard sale. He saw boxes of comic books for sale. He searched through the boxes for comic books he wanted to buy. In each of the first two boxes, he found eight comic books that he wanted. He found six comic books that he wanted in each of the next five boxes. How many comic books did he buy in all?

B. Caitlyn bought two boxes of pencils for $5. Each box had ten pencils in it. How much did each pencil cost?

C. The faculty lounge has five rows of teacher mailboxes with six boxes in each row. If Tanner wanted to put eight passes to the baseball game in each box, how many would he need?

D. The train at the zoo can hold 144 passengers at one time. If each seat can hold 4 passengers and each car has twelve seats, how many cars does the train have?

Can You Guess?

SHOW ME THE WAY

A. You have seven coins that total 92 cents. The coins include at least one quarter, one dime, one nickel, and one penny. What combination of coins do you have?

Strategic Steps

1 First, you know that there is a minimum of two pennies. That leaves 90 cents and five coins to discover.

2 One quarter, one dime, and one nickel added together equals 40 cents. That reduces the total to 50 cents and two coins you need to discover. The only combination of two coins that will add up to 50 cents is two quarters.

3 Add together all the coins, and you will have _____ quarter(s), _____ dime(s), _____ nickel(s), and _____ penny(ies).

B. The sum of two numbers is 26, and their product is 168. What are the two numbers?

Strategic Steps

1 Start by listing some of the numbers that will add up to 26. Since the product is large, that tells you the numbers will be large. Try 10 + 16 = 26. The addition is correct, but if you multiply the numbers, what product will you get?

$$16 \times 10 = \underline{\hspace{2cm}}$$

2 Is that number higher or lower than 168? If it is higher, you may want to find addends where one is lower. If it is lower, you may want to use larger addends. Try another set of numbers.

_____ + _____ = 26   _____ × _____ = _____

3 Continue trying numbers until you find the correct pair of addends.

Math Logic & Word Problems • 3–4 © 2005 Creative Teaching Press

Riddle Me a Number

SHOW ME THE WAY

A. Prateek started with a number.
Then he added 16.
Then he subtracted 4.
Then he added 5.
The result is 45.

What number did he start with? _____

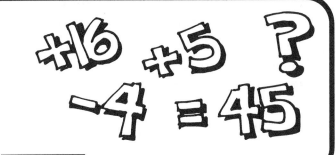

Strategic Steps

1 Your final number is 45. You need to work backward and do the opposite of what Prateek did. For the first step, you would subtract 5.

$$45 - 5 = \text{_____} \text{ (first number)}$$

2 Take that number and add 4 (the opposite of the next step).

$$\text{_____ (first number)} + 4 = \text{_____ (second number)}$$

3 Subtract 16 from that number.

$$\text{_____ (second number)} - 16 = \text{_____ (beginning number)}$$

4 To check your work, start with the beginning number and follow Prateek's steps to see if you end up with 45.

B. Andrew picked a number.
Then he multiplied it by 2.
Then he subtracted 15.
Then he added 12.
His final number was 27.

What number did he start with? _____

Math Logic & Word Problems • 3–4 © 2005 Creative Teaching Press

And the Answer Is...

A. Adelaide started with a number.
Then she divided by 3.
Then she added 24.
Then she multiplied by 2.
Her final number was 66.

What was her beginning number? _____

B. Shane started with a number.
Then he added 53.
Then he divided by 2.
Then he divided by 4.
His final number was 12.

What was his beginning number? _____

C. Robin picked her number.
She multiplied by 12.
Then she added 36.
Then she subtracted 65.
Her final number was 67.

What was her beginning number? _____

D. Frank picked a number.
Then he added 123.
Then he subtracted 44.
Then he divided by 10.
His final number was 15.

What was his beginning number? _____

Math Logic & Word Problems • 3–4 © 2005 Creative Teaching Press

Solve Our Riddles

Mrs. Marcus's students wrote number riddles and challenged their classmates to solve them. Can you solve them? Once you find the beginning number, go back and check your answer by following the steps of the riddle. If you end up with the same final number, you did it correctly.

A. Martin picked his number.
Then he added 254 to it.
Then he divided by 5.
Then he added 12.
His final number was 77.

What was his beginning number? _____

B. Cindy picked her number.
Then she divided by 6.
Then she added 2.
Then she multiplied by 5.
Her final number was 150.

What was her beginning number? _____

C. Tom picked his number.
Then he multiplied by 2.
Then he added 433.
Then he divided by 5.
His final number was 101.

What was his beginning number? _____

D. Leah picked her number.
Then she divided by 12.
Then she added 19.
Then she divided by 9.
Her final number was 3.

What was her beginning number? _____

The Toy Store

SHOW ME THE WAY

A. Sharon bought a new video for $9.98 and a new puzzle for $7.69. She paid with a $20.00 bill. How much change did she get?

Strategic Steps

1 First, add together the prices for the items that Sharon bought.

$9.98 + $7.69 = _____ (purchase total)

2 Now, subtract that total from the amount paid.

$20.00 − _____ = _____ (change)

B. Satara's weekly allowance is $5.00. Every week she saves $2.00 toward buying a new bookcase for her bedroom. The bookcase costs $48.99. How many weeks will it take her to save enough to buy the bookcase?

Strategic Steps

1 Estimate the cost of the bookcase to the nearest and higher even number of dollars. Since $48 is less than the bookcase will cost, use $50 as your estimate.

2 Divide $50 by 2 to discover how many weeks it will take to save the money.

$50 ÷ 2 = _____

Math Logic & Word Problems • 3–4 © 2005 Creative Teaching Press

Allowances

A. Zack's weekly allowance is $4.00. Each week he spends $1.00 on video games and $1.50 on comic books, and he saves $1.25 toward buying new computer games. How much does he have left over every week?

B. Larry went to the grocery store for his mom. He bought bread for $1.09, bananas for $2.45, and eggs for $1.39. He paid with a $10.00 bill. How much change did he get?

C. Heather went to a carnival with her friends. Her admission ticket cost $7.00. She spent $1.50 for a bottle of water. Then she spent $7.50 on tickets for rides. She had $20.00 when she left home. How much money did she have left at the end of the day?

D. Charles has been saving to buy a new camera. The camera he likes costs $63.00. He has $48.75 in savings and is able to save $2.25 per week toward the camera. How many more weeks does he need to save until he can buy the camera?

E. The movie Frances has been waiting to see opens tonight. Frances knows the movie tickets cost $4.50 each. She is estimating $5.00 for popcorn and $3.00 for a soda. After the movie, she and her friends want to go out for ice cream. If Frances takes $15.00, how much money will she have left to buy ice cream?

Math Logic & Word Problems • 3–4 © 2005 Creative Teaching Press

The Carnival

Parkview Elementary School is having a carnival. There will be 30 different games, each costing 1 ticket to play. The tickets are sold in booklets of 5 for $1.00. The PTA is selling hot dog meals for $4.00 each.

A. Crystal has been saving her money to buy tickets for the games at the school carnival. She wants to take her little brother Ian with her. If she wants to buy 30 tickets and two hot dog meals, how much money will she need?

B. John, Keisha, Jimmy, and Fiona all collected aluminum cans to earn money to buy tickets for the games at the school carnival. They earned $8.44. How many carnival tickets can they get for that money? How many tickets will each friend get?

C. Tina's mother told her that the whole family would be going to the carnival. She wants Tina to find out how much it will cost to buy 100 tickets and five hot dog meals. Help Tina find out how much money they need.

D. Mr. Welch wants to buy enough tickets to give each of his 22 students 2 tickets. How many tickets will he need to buy, and how much will they cost?

E. There were 1,200 tickets sold for the carnival. The PTA also sold $240 in hot dog meals. How much money did the school make from the carnival?

Math Logic & Word Problems • 3–4 © 2005 Creative Teaching Press

What Time Will It Be?

SHOW ME THE WAY

A. Your favorite show comes on at 6:00 p.m. You get out of school at 3:15 p.m. How long do you have to wait until your show starts?

_____

Strategic Steps

❶ Figure the minutes to reach the next hour by using subtraction. Remember there are 60 minutes in 1 hour.

60 – 15 = _____ minutes until 4:00 p.m.

❷ Count the hours between 4:00 p.m. and 6:00 p.m.

❸ Add the minutes and hours.

_____ hours and _____ minutes

B. Grace went to her friend's house at 4:30 p.m. She stayed for 90 minutes. What time did she get home?

_____

Strategic Steps

❶ Figure how many hours are in 90 minutes.

90 minutes = _____ hour and _____ minutes

❷ Count forward 1 hour from 4:30 p.m., and add 30 minutes.

In a Hurry?

A. Courtney needs to be at swim practice in 15 minutes. What time does swim practice start? Swim practice lasts for 45 minutes. What time will she finish?

B. Kayley is going to the movies with her friend at 6:15 p.m. It is now 4:45 p.m. She has 45 minutes of homework, 15 minutes to clean her room, and 30 minutes to eat dinner. Will she be able to finish all these things in time to go to the movies?

C. John's family is flying to visit his grandmother in Boston. The flight is leaving at 8:30 a.m. and will take 2 hours and 45 minutes. What time will they arrive in Boston?

D. The first clock below shows what time Shin and Adam started out on the hiking trail. The second clock shows what time they finished. How long did it take them to hike the trail?

Started hiking   Finished hiking

Math Logic & Word Problems • 3–4 © 2005 Creative Teaching Press

Name _____ Date _____

Is It Time Yet?

A. Malik was cooking dinner in a slow cooker. He started the stew at 10:00 a.m., and it cooked for 6 hours. What time was it ready?

B. Dylan was playing outside and realized it was 10:45 a.m. He needs to be at his friend Mitchell's house at 11:45 a.m. It takes 15 minutes to walk to Mitchell's house. How long does he have to get ready?

C. Ryan checked a book out of the library today. He sat down at 12:30 p.m. and started reading it. It took him 3 hours and 15 minutes to finish the book. What time did he finish?

D. The first clock shows what time Tiffany arrived home from school. The second clock shows what time dinner will be ready. How much time does Tiffany have to play?

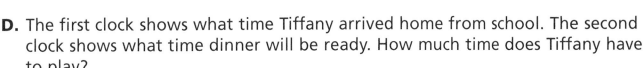

Home from school   Dinner

Math Logic & Word Problems • 3–4 © 2005 Creative Teaching Press

Let's Double

SHOW ME THE WAY

Mrs. Bartee was given a bromeliad as a Christmas gift one year. Bromeliads are very interesting plants. The parent plant will bloom once in a lifetime and then will produce two "pups" or small plants that grow at the base of the parent. The parent will die, and the two smaller plants will grow. This way, the plants will double in number every year. The following chart shows what happened to the bromeliads over the first few years.

Year	Blooms
1	1
2	2
3	4
4	8
5	

Year	Blooms
6	
7	
8	
9	
10	

How many plants will be in the class at the end of ten years? Make a prediction, and then work to see if you are right. How close is the calculation to your prediction?

Strategic Steps

1 Use the charts to see how the plants doubled over a period of four years. Write down your 10-year prediction.

_____

2 Now, continue the chart to show what happens over the next six years. Each year the number of plants will double. Use the blank chart to record your work.

3 Compare your prediction and the number you calculated. How close were you?

_____

Math Logic & Word Problems • 3–4 © 2005 Creative Teaching Press

Science Experiment

Lina and Courtney are raising a colony of amoebae as part of their science project. To reproduce, an amoeba will divide into two parts, forming two new amoebae. Each generation will double the number of amoebae.

Courtney and Lina are trying to estimate how many amoebae they will have in 10 and 20 generations. Here is the data they have collected from the first few generations:

Generation	Amoebae
1	1
2	2
3	4
4	8
5	
6	
7	
8	
9	
10	

Generation	Amoebae
11	
12	
13	
14	
15	
16	
17	
18	
19	
20	

Predict how many amoebae there will be after 10 generations. _____

Predict how many amoebae there will be after 20 generations. _____

Fill in the chart, and find out how many amoebae there are after

10 generations _____

20 generations _____

Charlotte's Decision

Charlotte was collecting money for a charity walk with her class. Her father offered to give her either one penny doubled every day for ten days or $5. Which should she choose?

Make a chart or diagram to show how much a penny doubled every day for ten days would equal.

Math Logic & Word Problems • 3–4 © 2005 Creative Teaching Press

Decimals

SHOW ME THE WAY

A. Yesterday, Sheri mowed 0.3 of the backyard. This morning she mowed another 0.2 of the yard. How much more does she have to mow?

_____

Strategic Steps

1 The first step is to add together the two decimals. Using vertical addition, line up the decimals and then add:

$$\begin{array}{r} 0.3 \\ + \ 0.2 \\ \hline \end{array}$$

2 Now, subtract from 1 to represent the entire yard.

$$\begin{array}{r} 1.00 \\ - \ \underline{} \\ \end{array}$$ (answer from #1)

B. Kathy, Lara, Madison, Aaron, and Wesley were practicing for a track meet. They each ran during practice today. Use the chart to see how much each friend ran, and then put the friends in order from who ran the fewest miles to the most miles.

Name	Kathy	Lara	Madison	Aaron	Wesley
Miles	1.2	1.5	0.12	2.01	0.64

Strategic Steps

1 First, go by the whole number. A larger whole number will be a larger number, regardless of the decimals following it.

2 Now, look at the number in the tenths place. The larger the number, the closer it will be to the next whole number.

Math Logic & Word Problems • 3–4 © 2005 Creative Teaching Press

More Decimals

A. Pat bought his dog Spot a bag of dog food. Spot ate 0.3 of the bag on Monday. On Tuesday Spot ate 0.4 of the bag. How much of the bag will be left for Spot to eat on Wednesday?

B. The school secretary was making copies of flyers to send home with all the students in the school. She used 1.3 packs of paper in the morning. She then used another 3.4 packs of paper in the afternoon. If she had 7 packs of paper when she began, how many are left?

C. Nick was cleaning up after the PTA meeting. He collected all the opened and unopened juice bottles. There were 1.2 bottles of apple juice, 2 bottles of grape juice, 1.7 bottles of cranberry juice, and 0.3 bottle of fruit punch. How much drink was left after the meeting?

D. Kara's family is buying a lot to build a new house. They looked at five lots and are trying to find the largest one. The lots are 1.7 acres, 0.5 acre, 2.3 acres, 1.75 acres, and 1.3 acres. Put the lots in order from smallest to largest.

Cameron's Day

A. For breakfast Cameron drank 0.4 cup of water and 0.8 cup of orange juice. If he needs to drink 2 cups of beverage for breakfast, how much more beverage does he need to drink?

B. On the bus ride home from school, Cameron read 0.2 of his history chapter. That afternoon he read another 0.4 of the chapter. How much does he have left to read after dinner?

C. Cameron weighed the animals in his toy collection. The table below shows the weights. Put the animals in order from greatest to least weight.

Animal	Weight
Fox	0.75 lb.
Beaver	1.20 lb.
Deer	1.34 lb.
Alligator	0.83 lb.
Buffalo	0.98 lb.

Animal	Weight

D. Cameron and his dad have been working on building a model train layout. In the first month, they put down 3.2 feet of track. In the second month, they put down 1.4 feet of track. In the third month, they finished the project by adding an additional 4.7 feet of track. How long was the completed track?

The Hardware Store

SHOW ME THE WAY

Joe is building a tree fort and needs to buy some items at the hardware store.

A. Joe needs 78 feet of boards for the floor. The boards come in 12-foot lengths. How many boards will he need?

Strategic Steps

1 Round the feet of boards Joe needs to the nearest 10 feet.   __80 feet__

2 Now, divide 80 by 12 to find how many boards he will need to buy. _____

B. Joe needs 127 nails to put down the floor. The size nail he needs has 10 nails in a pound. How many pounds of nails does he need to buy?

Strategic Steps

1 Round the number of nails Joe needs up to the nearest 10. _____

2 Now, divide that number by 10. _____ ÷ 10 = _____

C. Joe is going to build a ladder from 2 × 4 boards. He needs 36 feet of the boards. Each board is 8 feet long. How many boards will he need? _____

D. Joe needs nuts and bolts to attach the rungs to the railings while building the ladder. He needs a total of 24 nuts and 24 bolts. Each package contains 5 nuts and 5 bolts. How many packages will he need? _____

Math Logic & Word Problems • 3–4 © 2005 Creative Teaching Press

Name _____ Date _____

The Family Reunion

Valerie's family is having a reunion this weekend, and she's in charge of buying the items for the picnic lunch. The menu includes hot dogs, potato salad, and apple pie. There will be 34 people attending the family reunion.

A. Hot dogs are sold in packages of 10. How many packages will Valerie need to buy?

B. Hot dog buns are sold in packages of 8. How many packages will Valerie need to buy?

C. Valerie estimates she needs ½ cup of potato salad per person. Potato salad is sold in 4-cup containers. How many containers will Valerie need to buy?

D. The apple pies will each be cut into six slices. How many pies will Valerie need to buy?

E. Valerie also needs to buy paper plates, tableware, and cups for everyone. Each of these items is sold in packages of 12. How many packages of each will she need to buy?

Paper plates _____   Tableware _____   Cups _____

Math Logic & Word Problems • 3–4 © 2005 Creative Teaching Press

The Party

Jack is planning his birthday party. He is making a list of all the supplies and food he and his mom need to buy. They have had replies from 16 guests, plus Jack and his parents, for a total of 19 people.

A. Jack needs to order a birthday cake. The local bakery sells cakes based on servings in multiples of 4. If Jack wants to have enough cake left for his family to have some for dessert the next day, how many servings should the cake that he orders have?

B. Jack wants to decorate with balloons. He wants to have 275 balloons. Balloons are sold in bags of 14. How many bags will he need?

C. Jack's mother is making treat bags for everyone. The bags are sold in packages of 12. How many packages will she need to buy?

D. The yo-yos Jack wants to put in the treat bags are sold in packages of 6. How many packages will he need to buy?

Math Logic & Word Problems • 3–4 © 2005 Creative Teaching Press

Guess the Ages

SHOW ME THE WAY

A. Wayne is 4 years older than his friend Judy. Their ages add up to 16.

How old is Wayne? _____   How old is Judy? _____

Strategic Steps

1 We know that Wayne is 4 years older than Judy. We know that their ages together equal 16.

2 If we subtract the 4 (difference in their ages) from the 16, we will get 12. Then we can divide that number by 2 and we will get 6, which is Judy's age.

3 Wayne's age is Judy's age plus 4, so he will be 6 (Judy's age) + 4 = _____.

4 To check your answer, add together the ages to see if they equal 16.

6 + _____ = 16

All in the Family

A. David is 5 years older than his sister Mia. Their ages add up to 21.

How old is David? _____

How old is Mia? _____

B. Jose and Milo are twins. In 8 years, their ages will add up to 20.

How old are Jose and Milo today? _____

C. Lisa is 3 years older than her sister Laura. Together, their ages add up to 29.

How old is Lisa? _____

How old is Laura? _____

D. Cole's dad is ½ the age of his grandfather. The ages of Cole's dad and grandfather add up to 96.

How old is Cole's dad? _____

How old is Cole's grandfather? _____

Math Logic & Word Problems • 3–4 © 2005 Creative Teaching Press

How Old?

A. Timothy is 5 years older than Amanda. Amanda's mom is 37 years old. Together, Timothy's and Amanda's ages equal the age of Amanda's mom.

How old is Timothy? _____

How old is Amanda? _____

B. Manuel is ½ as old as his uncle. Together, their ages add up to 42.

How old is Manuel? _____

How old is his uncle? _____

C. Shi Ann is twice as old as her cousin. Together, their ages add up to the age of her aunt who is twice as old as 9-year-old Mary.

How old is Shi Ann's aunt? _____

How old is Shi Ann? _____

How old is Shi Ann's cousin? _____

D. In 5 years, Leroy will be twice as old as his brother. Today, their ages add up to 14.

How old is Leroy? _____

How old is his brother? _____

What Is Missing?

SHOW ME THE WAY

A. A number multiplied by 5 equals 30. What is the number? _____

B. After dividing a group of pumpkins into three groups, each group has four pumpkins. How many pumpkins did you start with? _____

C. I multiply a number by 3 and I get 36. What is the number? _____

D. _____ ÷ 6 = 28   8 × _____ = 72

E. When you add 7 to me, I equal 13. What number am I? _____

F. When you subtract 12 from me, I equal 14. What number am I? _____

Strategic Step

❶ For each of these problems, you need to write a number sentence with the information you have and then work backward to solve the number sentence.

For example, in problem A, you will divide 30 by 5 to get the answer:

$$30 ÷ 5 = 6$$

Check your answer: $$5 × 6 = 30$$

Math Logic & Word Problems • 3–4 © 2005 Creative Teaching Press

Missing Numbers

A. A number multiplied by 8 equals 40. What is the number?

B. After dividing the tennis balls into four groups, each group has six balls. How many balls did you start with?

C. Five groups of a number equal 30. What is the number?

D. $9 \div$ _____ $= 3$ $\qquad\qquad$ $28 -$ _____ $= 6$

E. I multiply a number by 6, and the answer is 42. What is the number I multiplied?

F. I divide a number by 3, and the answer is 11. What number did I divide?

Something Is Missing

A. A number multiplied by 12 equals 108. What is the number?

B. A number plus 14 equals 47. What is the number?

C. Jamila has divided her stuffed animals into twelve equal groups. Each group has four animals. How many animals did she have when she started?

D. _____ ÷ 2 = 34   14 × _____ = 84

   87 ÷ _____ = 29   35 − _____ = 8

E. I multiply a number by 12, and the answer is 72. What is the number I multiplied?

F. I divide a number by 8, and the answer is 21. What number did I divide?

Math Logic & Word Problems • 3–4 © 2005 Creative Teaching Press

Magic Squares

SHOW ME THE WAY

Magic squares have been around for hundreds of years. In reality, there is nothing "magic" about them. They are simply a pattern of numbers arranged in a manner where all rows and columns will add up to the same number. Each number will only appear once in a magic square.

For the following magic square, fill in the missing numbers. All columns and rows will add up to 15. Do not use a number more than once or repeat a number already used.

4		2
3		
8	1	6

Strategic Steps

1 The first thing known about this square is that all columns and rows will add up to 15. If you look at the top row, you are given the numbers 4 and 2. The first step is to add those together.

4 + 2 = _____ Subtract that sum from 15.

15 − _____ = _____ Use that number to fill in the blank square in the top row.

2 The second row is more difficult because it has two blanks. Instead of looking at the second row, let's look at the second column. You have determined that _____ is the missing number in the first row, so add that to the 1 from the third row.

_____ + 1 = _____ Subtract that sum from 15.

15 − _____ = _____ Put that number in the middle square.

3 Finally, you need to find the middle number of the third column. You know that the given numbers are 2 and 6.

2 + 6 = _____ Subtract that sum from 15.

15 − _____ = _____ Put that number in the remaining blank square.

4 To check your work, add up the numbers in all the rows and columns, and then in the diagonals, to make sure they each equal 15.

Is It Magic?

Magic squares have been around for hundreds of years. In reality, there is nothing "magic" about them. They are simply a pattern of numbers arranged in a manner where all rows and columns will add up to the same number. Each number will only appear once in a magic square.

In this magic square, all the columns and rows add up to 18.
Fill in the missing numbers.

9		8
5		
		3

In this magic square, all the columns and rows add up to 21.
Fill in the missing numbers.

10		
3	7	
		4

Math Logic & Word Problems • 3–4 © 2005 Creative Teaching Press

Fill in the Blanks

In this magic square, all the columns and rows add up to 12.
Fill in the missing numbers.

7		3
	4	8
		1

In this magic square, all the columns and rows add up to 69.
Fill in the missing numbers.

	34	24
	23	

In this magic square, all the columns and rows add up to 34.
Fill in the missing numbers.

16		2	13
	10	11	
9			12
	15		

Patterns

SHOW ME THE WAY

A. In this pattern, what three numbers would come next?

2, 4, 6, 8, _____, _____, _____

Strategic Step

❶ Look at the numbers, and see what the pattern is. In this case, each number goes up by 2.

B. Draw the next three shapes in this pattern.

 ,  ,  _____, _____, _____

Strategic Step

❶ Look for the shapes to start repeating themselves.

C. Identify the next three items in this pattern.

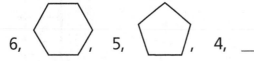

6, ⬡ , 5, ⬠ , 4, _____, _____, _____

Strategic Step

❶ Look for a relationship between the number and the shape.

Math Logic & Word Problems • 3–4 © 2005 Creative Teaching Press

Find the Pattern

A. In this pattern, what three numbers would come next?

2, 4, 8, 16, _____, _____, _____

B. In this pattern, what three numbers would come next?

12, 10, 8, _____, _____, _____

C. Draw the next three shapes in this pattern.

_____, _____, _____

D. Identify the next three fractions in this pattern.

½, ⅓, ¼, ⅕, _____, _____, _____

E. In this pattern, what three numbers would come next?

10, 21, 32, 43, _____, _____, _____

Math Logic & Word Problems • 3–4 © 2005 Creative Teaching Press

More Patterns

A. Fill in the missing numbers to complete the pattern.

_____, 4, 6, _____, 10, _____

B. Fill in the missing shapes to complete the pattern.

C. Fill in the missing fractions to complete the pattern.

_____, ⅙, ⅕, _____, ⅓, _____

D. Fill in the missing shapes to complete the pattern.

E. Fill in the missing numbers to complete the pattern.

1, 1, 2, 3, 5, _____, 13, _____, 34

Math Logic & Word Problems • 3–4 © 2005 Creative Teaching Press

Guess My Number

SHOW ME THE WAY

I am in the square.
I am an even number.
I am also in the rectangle.
I am also in the triangle.

What number am I?

_____

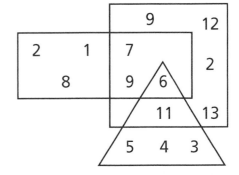

Strategic Steps

1 Cross out all the numbers that are not in the square.

2 Cross out any odd numbers in the square.

3 Circle any numbers that are in both the rectangle and the square.

4 Your answer is the one number that is shared by the square, triangle, and rectangle.

What Number Am I?

A.

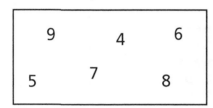 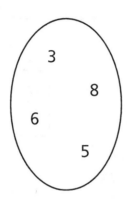 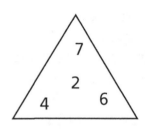

I am in the triangle.
I am in the rectangle.
I am not in the oval.
I am an even number.

What number am I? _____

B.

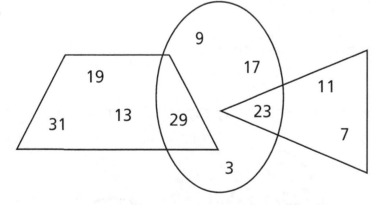

I am a prime number.
I am larger than 10 and smaller than 25.
I am in the oval.
I am not in the triangle.

What number am I? _____

Math Logic & Word Problems • 3–4 © 2005 Creative Teaching Press

Find a Number

A.

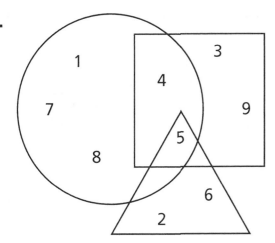

I am an even number.
I am less than 5.
I am in the square.

What number am I? _____

B.

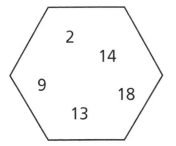

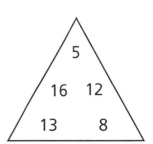

I am an even number.
I am larger than 10.
I am not in the triangle.
I am in the square.
I am also in the hexagon.

What number am I? _____

Area Puzzles

SHOW ME THE WAY

The **area** of a shape is the amount of space the shape covers. The area is determined by multiplying the length times the width of the shape.

A. Aisha wanted new carpet for her room. Her bedroom is 14 feet long and 11 feet wide. How much carpet will she need?

_____

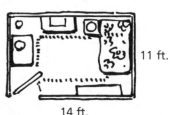

11 ft.

14 ft.

Strategic Step

❶ To determine the area you need to multiply the length times the width. For this problem, you would multiply the following:

14 feet × 11 feet = _____ square feet

B. Christian has an area of 116 square feet in his yard to put a swimming pool. He found an ad for a rectangular pool that is 10 feet by 12 feet. His parents said that they would buy the pool if Christian could show them that it would fit in his yard. Did they buy the pool?

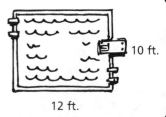

10 ft.

12 ft.

Strategic Steps

❶ To find the answer to this problem, you first need to find the area of the pool. To do this, you multiply the length times the width.

10 feet × 12 feet = _____ (don't forget the units)

❷ Now, compare the area of the pool and the area of Christian's yard. If the area of the pool is larger than the yard, then his parents will not buy it for him. If the area of the pool is smaller than the yard, then they will buy it.

Math Logic & Word Problems • 3–4 © 2005 Creative Teaching Press

What Is the Area?

The **area** of a shape is the amount of space the shape covers. The area is determined by multiplying the length times the width of the shape.

A. Rose wants to compare the area of her front yard and backyard. The front yard has a length of 45 meters and a width of 20 meters. The backyard has a length of 45 meters and a width of 25 meters.

Front	20 m

45 m

Back	25 m

45 m

What is the area of the front yard? _____

What is the area of the backyard? _____

How many more square meters does the larger yard have? _____

B. Elizabeth wants to make carpeting to go in the living room of the dollhouse she is building. The room measures 8 inches by 7 inches. What is the area she needs to cover?

C. Juan wants to replace the rectangular concrete patio in the backyard. It measures 14 feet on one side and 15 feet on the next side. Each bag of concrete will cover an area of 10 square feet. How many bags does Juan need to buy?

Assignment Area

The **area** of a shape is the amount of space the shape covers. The area is determined by multiplying the length times the width of the shape.

A. Elizabeth and Sean were assigned to find the areas of the following items:

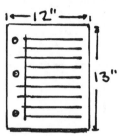

Notebook paper

_____

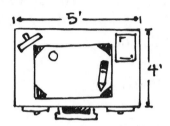

Teacher's desk

_____

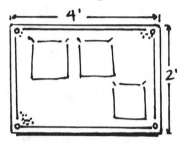

Bulletin board

_____

Help them find the area of each item.

B. Once Elizabeth and Sean were finished, they were given this assignment: Order the items from the smallest area to the largest area.

C. Roman is helping his father replace the bathroom floor. The floor measures 8 feet by 10 feet. The tiles they are using each cover 1 square foot. How many tiles do they need to cover the entire floor?

10 ft.

8 ft.

Math Logic & Word Problems • 3–4 © 2005 Creative Teaching Press

Perimeter in the Home

SHOW ME THE WAY

> **Perimeter** is the distance around a figure. You find the perimeter by adding together the lengths of the sides.
>
> **A.** Lilley's grandmother is teaching her to make a quilt. The sides of her squares are each 15 centimeters. What is the perimeter of each quilt square?

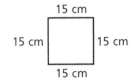

Strategic Step

❶ To find the perimeter, you add together the lengths of the sides. Since all four sides of a square are equal lengths, you can take the length and multiply by 4.

15 centimeters × 4 = _____ centimeters

> **B.** Kayla is baking a sheet cake for a party. She wants to put a decorative edge along the bottom of the cake. She has approximately 40 inches of icing left. If the cake is a rectangle with one side 9 inches and the other side 14 inches, will she have enough icing to add the decorative edge?

Strategic Steps

❶ First, find the perimeter of the cake. To find the perimeter of a rectangle you add together the four sides. In this case, you know that the short sides are 9 inches and the long sides are 14 inches. Add those numbers together, and then multiply by 2.

9 inches + 14 inches = _____ inches

_____ inches × 2 = _____ inches (perimeter of the cake)

❷ Then, compare the perimeter of the cake with 40 inches. If it is smaller than 40 inches, Kayla has enough icing. If it is longer than 40 inches, she does not have enough icing.

Perimeter Puzzlers

Perimeter is the distance around a figure. You find the perimeter by adding together the lengths of the sides. The rectangle shown has a perimeter of 20 feet.

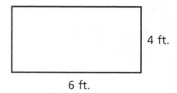

Solve the perimeter problems.

A. Mr. Kent is building a playhouse for his children. The floor is in the shape of a rectangle. One side of the floor is 16 feet long. The other side is half as long. What is the perimeter of the floor?

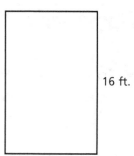

B. Mr. Kent is making a window frame that is shaped like a rectangle. Each half of the rectangle forms a square. Each side of the square is 2 meters. What is the perimeter of the window frame?

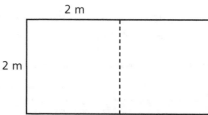

C. The fence around the yard is a rectangle. One side of the fence is 9 meters long. The other side is 12 meters long. What is the perimeter of the yard?

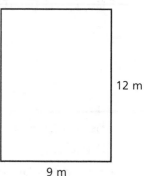

Math Logic & Word Problems • 3–4 © 2005 Creative Teaching Press

Mr. Dennis's Assignment

You can determine the perimeter of all different shapes. Mr. Dennis asked his class to find a shape in their home or on the way home from school and find the perimeter of the item.

A. Joy measured a stop sign and discovered that all eight sides were 6 inches long. What is the perimeter of the stop sign?

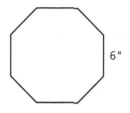

6"

B. Khaliq measured a box that his dad keeps on his desk. The box has five sides that measure 5 centimeters, 3 centimeters, 7 centimeters, 3 centimeters, and 5 centimeters. What is the perimeter of the box?

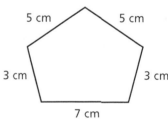

5 cm   5 cm

3 cm   3 cm

7 cm

C. Kaitlin measured her bedroom. The width is 2 feet shorter than the length. The length of Kaitlin's bedroom is 11 feet. What is the perimeter of Kaitlin's room?

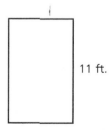

11 ft.

D. Todd measured the patio and discovered that the length is 3 feet more than the width. The width of the patio is 15 feet. What is the perimeter of the patio?

15 ft.

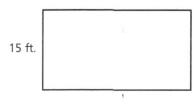

Which Do I Choose?

SHOW ME THE WAY

For each problem, determine if you need to find the area (length × width) or perimeter (add the lengths of all sides). Then write a number sentence that shows how to solve the problem.

A. The Smiths' backyard measures 40 feet by 60 feet. They want to put a fence around the yard. How much fencing do they need?

Strategic Steps

1 Draw a picture of what you need to find, and label all the parts.

2 Use your sketch to decide if you are trying to find the amount of space inside the square or rectangle, or the distance around it. In this case, you want to find the distance around the yard, so you need to find the perimeter.

40 feet + 60 feet = _____ feet × 2 = _____ feet

B. Kelley's father is building a raised flower garden. He needs to find out how much soil to buy to fill the garden. For each square foot, he needs to buy one bag of soil. The garden will measure 3 feet by 5 feet. How many bags of soil will Kelley's dad need?

Strategic Steps

1 Draw a picture or diagram to show what you are trying to find.

2 For this problem, you need to find the space inside the rectangle, so you need to find the area. Write a number sentence, and find the square feet. That number will be how many bags of soil Kelley's father will need.

Math Logic & Word Problems • 3–4 © 2005 Creative Teaching Press

 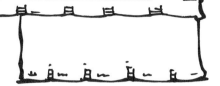

School Play

Area is the measure of the space inside a polygon; **perimeter** is the measure of the distance along the sides of the polygon. To find the area of a square or rectangle, you will multiply the length times the width. To find the perimeter, you will add together the lengths of all the sides.

For each problem, determine if you need to find the area or perimeter. Then, write a number sentence that shows how to solve the problem.

Logan is preparing for the school play. He needs to find out information to get started.

A. He needs to put a curtain around the stage. To do this, he needs to install rods in the ceiling around the section for the curtain. The stage is 24 feet by 18 feet. How many feet of rod does Logan need?

B. Logan wants to build a set that will look like a pond. He needs to paint a pond that is 3 feet by 2 feet. How much of the set will be painted?

C. Logan is building a door set and wants to put trim around the door. The door measures 6 feet by 3 feet. How much trim does he need?

D. The final scene will require a background that will be painted to look like the night sky. This background section will measure 6 feet by 8 feet. How much of the set will Logan need to paint?

Area or Perimeter?

Area is the measure of the space inside a polygon; **perimeter** is the measure of the distance along the sides of the polygon. To find the area of a square or rectangle, you will multiply the length times the width. To find the perimeter, you will add together the lengths of all the sides.

For each problem, determine if you need to find the area or perimeter. Then, write a number sentence that shows how to solve the problem.

Juliet was putting in a garden this year so she could grow vegetables for her family. Her garden plot is 12 feet by 9 feet.

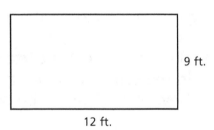

9 ft.

12 ft.

A. Juliet wants to put a fence around her garden. How much fencing will she need?

B. Juliet wants to add a layer of enriched soil. She will add one bag of soil for every square foot of garden. How much soil will she need?

C. Juliet wants to get a tarp to cover the garden in the early spring to protect the young seedlings. What size tarp will she need?

Math Logic & Word Problems • 3–4 © 2005 Creative Teaching Press

Congruency

SHOW ME THE WAY

Congruent figures have the same size and shape.

This pair of rectangles is congruent because they are the same size and shape, even though they are arranged differently.

2 in. | 4 in.
4 in. | 2 in.

Label each pair of figures **congruent** or **not congruent**.

2 cm
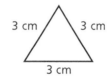 2 cm

1 cm
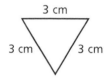 1 cm

A. _____

3 cm 3 cm

3 cm

3 cm
 3 cm 3 cm

B. _____

1 cm

1 cm

C. _____

1 cm 1 cm

Strategic Steps

1 Remember that congruent figures are the same size but may be pointing in different directions. In the first example, the shapes are both squares. However, the size is different; one has sides that are 1 centimeter, and the other has sides that are 2 centimeters. If congruent figures must be the same shape (as these are) and the same size, are these two squares congruent?

2 In the second example, don't be fooled by the fact that the triangles are pointing in different directions. They both have the same size sides, so will they be congruent?

3 In this example, you are looking at two figures that both have all sides that are 1 centimeter. However, are they the same shape? If they aren't, then the figures are not congruent.

Pottery

Congruent figures have the same size and shape.

The Ancestral Puebloans used all sorts of shapes to decorate their pottery. Using what you know about congruent figures, add shapes to the following pots.

A. Draw two congruent shapes on this pot.

B. Draw four or more shapes that are not congruent on this pot.

C. Draw four or more shapes on this pot. Draw one set of congruent shapes and one set of shapes that are not congruent.

Math Logic & Word Problems • 3–4 © 2005 Creative Teaching Press

Congruent or Not?

Congruent figures have the same size and shape.

A. Are these shapes congruent? Explain your answer.

_____

_____

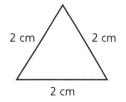

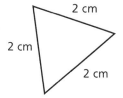

B. Are these shapes congruent? Explain your answer.

_____

_____

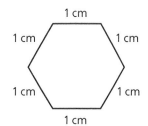

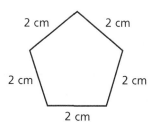

C. Draw a congruent shape next to each shape.

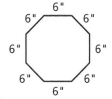

D. Draw a shape that is not congruent next to each figure.

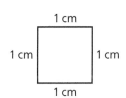

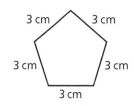

Shape Puzzles

SHOW ME THE WAY

Solve each riddle and draw the shape.

A. I am a quadrilateral.
All my sides are equal.
All my angles are 90 degrees.
What am I?

_____

B. I have three sides.
One of my angles is 90 degrees.
What am I?

_____

C. I have no sides.
I am perfectly round.
What am I?

_____

D. I have four sides.
All my angles are 90 degrees.
My top and bottom are the same length.
My sides are the same but different from the top.
What am I?

_____

Strategic Step

1 As you read the clues, draw a picture in your mind (or on paper). Adjust the picture as you read each clue.

Math Logic & Word Problems • 3–4 © 2005 Creative Teaching Press

Quadrilaterals, Triangles, and Circles, Oh My!

Solve each riddle and draw the shape.

A. I am a quadrilateral.
My angles may or may not be 90 degrees.
I have two sets of parallel sides.
What am I?

_____

B. I am a polygon.
I have more than four sides but less than six sides.
There is a building in Washington, D.C., named after me.
What am I?

_____

C. I am a polygon.
I have more than four sides.
Stop signs use my shape.
What am I?

_____

D. I have four sides.
Two of my sides are equal in length.
Two of my sides are parallel.
Two of my sides are not equal in length.
What am I?

_____

Math Logic & Word Problems • 3–4 © 2005 Creative Teaching Press

Riddle Me This

Solve each riddle and draw the shape.

A. I have four sides.
All my sides are equal in length.
My angles are not 90 degrees.
What am I?

_____

B. I am a polygon.
I have two sets of parallel sides.
My angles are all equal.
What am I?

_____

C. I am a polygon.
Bees use my shape in honeycombs.
I have six sides.
What am I?

_____

D. I have no sides.
I am curved.
Instead of round, I am oblong.
What am I?

_____

Math Logic & Word Problems • 3–4 © 2005 Creative Teaching Press

Measure Up

Show Me the Way

A. At breakfast Carol opened a carton of juice with 36 ounces and had to divide it equally among her two sisters and herself. How much juice did each girl drink? _____

Strategic Step

❶ Choose the operation you will use, and then write and solve the number sentence. Remember to use ounces in your answer.

B. Mackenzie has 12 feet of string to use to make bracelets and necklaces. It takes 14 inches of string for each necklace and 8 inches for each bracelet. She wants to make matching bracelets and necklaces for four friends. How much string will be left when she is finished? _____

Strategic Steps

❶ Remember that there are 12 inches in a foot, so first convert the feet to inches.

12 feet × 12 inches/foot = _____ inches

❷ Calculate how much string is needed for all the necklaces and bracelets.

4 × 14 inches = _____ inches   4 × 8 inches = _____ inches
       (for necklaces)   (for bracelets)

❸ Now, add together the amount of string needed for the necklaces and bracelets.

_____ inches + _____ inches = _____ inches
(for necklaces)   (for bracelets)   (total amount needed)

❹ Subtract the amount needed from the number of inches you started with.

_____ inches – _____ inches = _____ inches
(started with)   (used)   (amount left over)

How Much?

A. Paige has a bag that contains 8 cups of flour. She uses 3 cups to make chocolate chip cookies. Then she uses 2 cups to make biscuits. How much flour is left in the bag?

B. Nolan made 64 ounces of lemonade. He poured 8-ounce glasses of lemonade for himself and four friends. Later, Nolan's sister and mother each had an 8-ounce glass of lemonade. How much lemonade was left?

C. Jared has a gallon container of milk. He knows there are 8 ounces in a cup, 2 cups in a pint, 2 pints in a quart, and 4 quarts in a gallon. He is going to make French toast for his friends after his sleepover tonight. He needs 3 cups of milk for the French toast, and then he will need enough milk for each of his eight friends to have an 8-ounce glass of milk to drink. Does he have enough milk?

Math Logic & Word Problems • 3–4 © 2005 Creative Teaching Press

Math All Around Us

A. After school Allison was trying to jump rope with 108 inches of rope. Her mother said she could cut the rope into three equal sections so that Allison and her two sisters could jump rope at the same time. How long will each of the new ropes be in inches? How long in feet?

B. At school the playground has an area of 145 square meters. The third and fourth grades both want to play at the same time. The fourth grade needs 74 square meters to play a game. How much space do the third graders have to play?

C. Maria and Noah are trying to find out how many laps around the backyard will equal 2 miles. They know that there are 5,280 feet in a mile. The path in the backyard they want to run has sections that are 120 feet, 134 feet, 140 feet, and 134 feet. How many laps would they have to make if they wanted to run 2 miles?

Changing Units
SHOW ME THE WAY

A. There are 5,280 feet in a mile. How many yards are there in 2 miles?

_____

Strategic Steps

1 First, find how many feet there are in 2 miles.

5,280 feet × 2 = _____ feet

2 There are 3 feet in a yard. The next step would be to divide the total number of feet by 3 to determine the number of yards.

_____ feet ÷ 3 feet/yard = _____ yards

B. Kali has 150 yards of kite string. How many inches of kite string does she have?

_____

Strategic Steps

1 First, find out how many inches are in a yard using the measurements you know. You know there are 12 inches in a foot and 3 feet in a yard.

12 inches × 3 = _____ inches in a yard

2 Now, multiply that number by 150 yards.

_____ × 150 = _____
(inches in a yard)   (inches in 150 yards)

Math Logic & Word Problems • 3–4 © 2005 Creative Teaching Press

How Many?

A. There are 12 inches in a foot and 3 feet in a yard. If a football field is 100 yards long, how many inches long is it?

12 *inches x1foot*

B. There are 1.6 kilometers in a mile. Garrett walked 2 miles. How many kilometers did he walk?

C. Madeline has 8 yards of ribbon. She needs 12 inches of ribbon to make a hair bow. How many hair bows can she make?

D. There are 1,000 meters in a kilometer. Amber rides her bicycle 0.5 kilometer to school. How many meters did she ride?

The Hiking Trip

Charlotte, Victoria, Kyong, Barbara, and Deana are going on a three-day hiking trip. The adventure company will have dinner ready when they reach camp each night and cook breakfast before they leave. The only thing the children need to carry is their clothing and lunch in a daypack. They are limited to 5 kilograms (5,000 grams) of weight to carry.

A. Charlotte's daypack weighs 0.5 kilogram when it is empty. She wants to carry the following items: a liter bottle of water weighing 1,400 grams, a poncho that weighs 200 grams, a jacket that weighs 1 kilogram, and a change of clothes that weighs 750 grams. She is trying to decide between taking a field guide on birds that weighs 2 kilograms or a small booklet about wildflowers in the park that weighs 500 grams. Which can she take and still be under her 5-kilogram weight limit?

B. Deana is trying to decide what items to take with her. She has laid out the following items on her bed. Help her pick the items she will carry. Remember that she needs to carry water, raingear, and a change of clothing.

Item	Weight
daypack	0.5 kilogram
1 liter of water	1,400 grams
1.5 liters of water	2 kilograms
rain jacket	1,200 grams
poncho	300 grams
outfit 1	750 grams
outfit 2	500 grams
outfit 3	1,500 grams
camera	500 grams
binoculars	1,200 grams
wildflower booklet	1,700 grams
bird field guide	500 grams

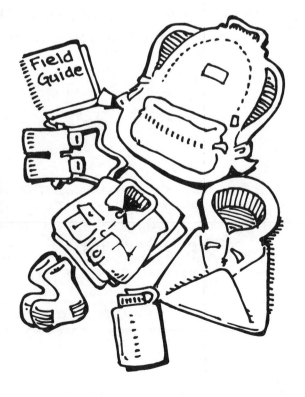

Which items can Deana take with her?

Math Logic & Word Problems • 3–4 © 2005 Creative Teaching Press

Baking Cookies

SHOW ME THE WAY

Cookie Recipe

Ingredient	Three Dozen	Six Dozen	Twelve Dozen
butter	1 cup		
sugar	2 cups		
eggs	2		
flour	3 cups		
walnuts	1 cup		
chocolate chips	1 cup		

A. Mrs. Gray Eagle was baking cookies for the school bake sale. Her recipe makes three dozen cookies, but she needs to make six dozen cookies. How much of each ingredient will she need?

Strategic Step

1 To go from three dozen to six dozen cookies, you will need to multiply each ingredient by 2. Instead of 1 cup of butter, you will need 2 times 1 cup of butter, or 2 cups. Instead of 2 cups of sugar, you will need 2 times 2 cups of sugar, or 4 cups. Fill in the "Six Dozen" column on the chart.

B. Mrs. Dawes wants to use the same recipe to make cookies to have as refreshments after the band concert. She needs twelve dozen cookies. How much of each ingredient will she need?

Strategic Step

1 To go from three dozen to twelve dozen, what number will you need to multiply by? Multiply all ingredients by that number. Fill in the "Twelve Dozen" column on the chart.

Birthday Party

A. Mrs. Sandy's class is planning a surprise birthday party for her. Debbie and Marcus are in charge of making the lemonade. How much of each ingredient will they need to make a 1-cup serving for 36 people?

Lemonade

Ingredient	4 Cups	36 Cups
lemons	3	
water	4 cups	
sugar	½ cup	

B. Helen and Glenn are going to bake brownies for the party. How much of each ingredient do they need for 36 servings?

Brownies

Ingredient	One Dozen	Three Dozen
unsweetened cocoa powder	½ cup	
flour	1 cup	
baking powder	1 teaspoon	
salt	½ teaspoon	
butter	½ cup	
eggs	2	
sugar	1½ cups	

Math Logic & Word Problems • 3–4 © 2005 Creative Teaching Press

Pizza Fun

Barry, Khaliq, Joy, and Gwen are going to have a pizza party for their friends. They have recipes for dough and sauce from the pizza parlor that Khaliq's father owns; but the recipes make too much, and they need to scale them down. They will be making only 5 pizzas.

Using the tables, find the amount of each ingredient needed to make only 5 pizzas.

Pizza Dough

Ingredient	10 Pizzas	5 Pizzas
warm water	9 cups	4 ½
active yeast	10 tablespoons	5
sugar	10 teaspoons	5
salt	5 teaspoons	2 ½
oil	20 tablespoons	10
flour	25 cups	12 ½

Pizza Sauce

Ingredient	25 Pizzas	5 Pizzas
tomatoes	10, medium-size	2
onions	5	1
sugar	5 teaspoons	1
fresh basil	10 teaspoons	2
garlic	15 cloves	3

How Much Do I Need?

SHOW ME THE WAY

You are making tuna casserole for dinner and need 2 cups of egg noodles. When you go to the store, all the packages are in ounces, not cups. From your cooking class at school, you remember that 2 ounces of egg noodles is ½ cup. Do you need to buy the 4-ounce, 6-ounce, or 12-ounce bag of egg noodles?

_____

Strategic Steps

1 The problem tells you that 2 ounces of egg noodles equals ½ cup. Now you need to find how many ½ cups are in 2 cups.

2 Since there are two ½ cup measures in 1 cup, you would multiply $2 \times 2 = 4$.

3 Now, multiply that number by 2 ounces. $4 \times 2 =$ _____ ounces

4 Which of the bags will have enough egg noodles for your recipe?

Math Logic & Word Problems • 3–4 © 2005 Creative Teaching Press

Now You're Cooking

A. Scott and Tanner are making macaroni and cheese for their camp group. There are 20 kids in the group. To make 20 servings of macaroni and cheese, Scott and Tanner need 10 cups of elbow macaroni. Elbow macaroni comes in bags that weigh 8 ounces or 16 ounces. One cup of elbow macaroni weighs 6 ounces. How many bags, and in which size, will give them enough macaroni to make the recipe?

B. Rashid is making vegetable soup for his family. The recipe calls for 4 cups of tomato juice. He has several cans of tomato juice, but the measure is in milliliters. He knows that 1 cup equals about 236 milliliters. The cans he has are two each of 250 milliliters, 500 milliliters, and 450 milliliters. Which of the cans will he need to make his soup?

C. Albert is learning how to make bean soup. The recipe calls for 4 cups of beans. Lentils are sold in bags of 4 ounces and 8 ounces. Albert has one 4-ounce bag of lentils and discovers that is ⅓ cup. How many bags in which sizes does Albert need to buy to make his soup?

D. Miranda is making punch. The recipe is in quarts, but the ingredients are only sold in liters. A 2-liter bottle of ginger ale is equal to 2 quarts, 3.6 ounces. She needs 9 quarts of ginger ale for the punch. How many 2-liter bottles will she need? (There are 32 ounces in a quart.)

Construction Woes

Maria was having a hectic day. At the construction site she manages, she wrote out notes for the construction crew. Jorge took her notes and typed them up, but Maria used the wrong units of measure. Please help him to correct the mistakes.

A. In the entryway, add 3 ounces (_____) of trim to the door.

B. Use 6 meters (_____) of paint on the walls.

C. In the living room, make the bookcase an additional liter (_____) to the side.

D. Install an electrical outlet 12 pounds (_____) from the corner.

E. In the bedroom, add 3 kilometers (_____) of trim over the window.

F. In the bathroom, use a 4-mile (_____) toilet instead of the 6-yard (_____) one that is in there now.

G. In the kitchen, make sure the sink can hold 2 acres (_____) of water.

H. The cabinets need to be 2 feet (_____) lower.

I. It looks like you will need 2 inches (_____) of paint for the garage floor.

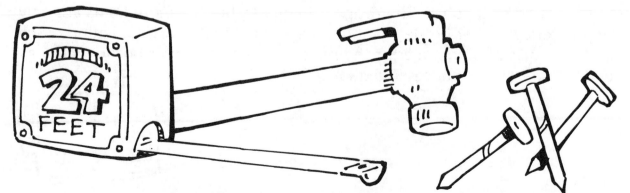

Math Logic & Word Problems • 3–4 © 2005 Creative Teaching Press

Cooking School

Gabrielle was spending the summer at a cooking school and sent home an excited letter the first week. Her brother thought it was funny that she made so many mistakes describing the things she was cooking. Help correct the letter by correcting the units of measure.

Dear Family,

   We are having so much fun cooking. Today, we used 1 inch

(_____) of milk along with an egg, ½ mile (_____) of sugar,

and 1 meter (_____) of vanilla to make French toast for breakfast.

   Lunch was a taco salad using 1 yard (_____) of washed and

torn lettuce, ¼ gallon (_____) of diced chicken, 1 kilometer

(_____) of olives, 1 yard (_____) of tomatoes, and 1 liter

(_____) of sour cream.

   Tonight for dinner we are having quiche made with eggs, 2 pounds

(_____) of cream, 1 centimeter (_____) of bacon, and 2 feet

(_____) of spinach.

                                          Love,

                                          Gabrielle

Name _____ Date _____

Wild West Adventures

Aaron was working for a travel agent and wrote a travel brochure for Wild West Adventures on his computer at home. His little brother Troy decided it would be fun to change all the units of measure. Help Aaron correct his brother's changes.

Visitors to Wild West Adventures will enter the park through a large 30-centimeter (_____) replica of a tepee. From the entrance, you walk 20 gallons (_____) to the main street.

The 10-yard (_____) saloon serves drinks and ice cream.

At ½ pint (_____) long, the Grizzly River rafting ride is one of the longest and fastest water rides in the west.

The Strawberry Hill train ride is 12 inches (_____) of track meandering through the hills.

Lunch will be an adventure as well. The drinks are served in 20-mile (_____) cups, and the plates will hold 2 acres (_____) of food.

Math Logic & Word Problems • 3–4 © 2005 Creative Teaching Press

Ice-Cream Toppings

SHOW ME THE WAY

Your favorite ice-cream toppings are chocolate chips, sprinkles, peanuts, and strawberries. You especially like ice-cream sundaes with two of those toppings at once. How many different combinations can you make?

Strategic Steps

1 List the possible combinations in order to count them. Remember that chocolate chips and peanuts are the same as peanuts and chocolate chips and should not be repeated.

Chocolate chips:	sprinkles
	peanuts
	strawberries

| Sprinkles: | peanuts |
| | strawberries |

Note: Sprinkles can be mixed with chocolate chips, but this combination is listed under chocolate chips and would not count a second time.

| Peanuts: | strawberries |

Note: Peanuts can also be mixed with chocolate chips or sprinkles, but these combinations were listed under other mixtures and would not count a second time.

| Strawberries: | no new mixtures |

2 Once you have your list, go back and count the topping pairs.

How many different pairs of toppings did you count? _____

Your Order, Please

Your family is going to try the new restaurant in town. They have an omelet bar, and everyone will be able to order an omelet with two fillings. The filling choices for omelets are cheese, mushrooms, peppers, onions, and tomatoes.

List the possible ingredient combinations.

Cheese ———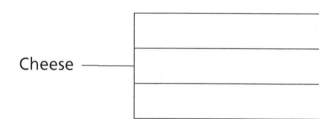

Mushrooms ———

Peppers ———

Onions ———————————————

Tomatoes ———————————————

How many different combinations did you find? _____

Math Logic & Word Problems • 3–4 © 2005 Creative Teaching Press

School Colors

Your school is having a Bright Color Day, and each day you will wear two arm bands in two of the following colors: red, blue, yellow, green, black, white, or purple. You and your classmates are trying to find out how many combinations there are to see if you can combine the colors and have each person wear a different combination.

List the different combinations.

Red: _____   _____   _____

             _____   _____   _____

Blue: _____   _____   _____

             _____   _____

Yellow: _____   _____   _____

             _____

Green: _____   _____   _____

Black: _____   _____

White: _____

Purple: _____

How many possible color combinations are there? _____

There are 22 students in your class. Can you each wear a different color combination? _____

Name _____ Date _____

Camp Activities

SHOW ME THE WAY

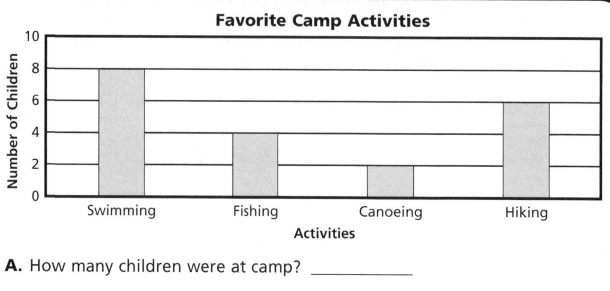

Favorite Camp Activities

A. How many children were at camp? _____

B. How many more children like hiking than fishing? _____

C. If you add together the number of children who like canoeing and fishing, it equals the number of children who like which activity? _____

Strategic Steps

1 To answer question A, add up the number of children who like each activity.

2 To answer question B, you will need to find out how many children like hiking and how many children like fishing. The phrase "how many more" tells you to use subtraction to find the answer.

Write your subtraction sentence: _____

3 To find the answer to question C, you will need to find out how many children like canoeing and how many children like fishing. The phrase "if you add together" tells you to use addition to find the answer.

Write your addition sentence: _____

Now compare that number to the other numbers on the graph, and find the activity with the same number of children as the sum in your addition sentence.

Math Logic & Word Problems • 3–4 © 2005 Creative Teaching Press

Name _____ Date _____

Sports

Mrs. Burke's class took a poll to see which sport each child liked. The results are shown on the bar graph.

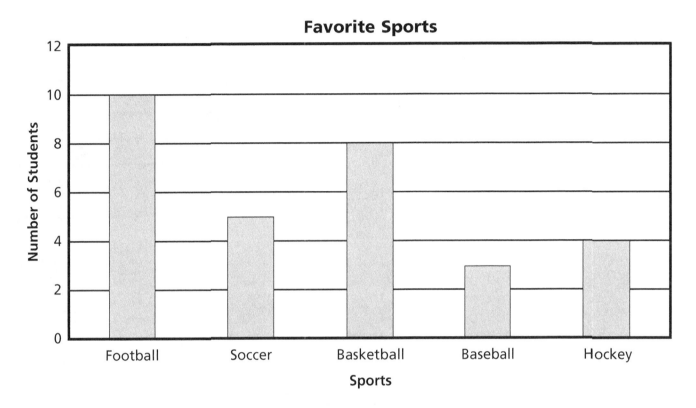

Favorite Sports

A. How many children like each sport?

Football: _____   Soccer: _____   Basketball: _____

Baseball: _____   Hockey: _____

B. How many children are there in Mrs. Burke's class? _____

C. How many more children like basketball than like hockey? _____

D. How many children like football, basketball, and baseball combined? _____

E. If you add together the number of children who like two of the sports, it would equal the number of children who like basketball. What are those two sports?

_____ and _____

Math Logic & Word Problems • 3–4 © 2005 Creative Teaching Press

Favorite Subject

Mrs. DeWitt's class voted on their favorite subject. The clues below will help you find how many children like each subject.

- Two more students like math than like science.
- Half the number of students who like science like history.
- The number of students who like reading equals the number of students who like math and science combined.
- Two students like history.

A. How many students like each subject?

Math _____   Reading _____

Science _____   History _____

B. Use the numbers to create a bar graph.

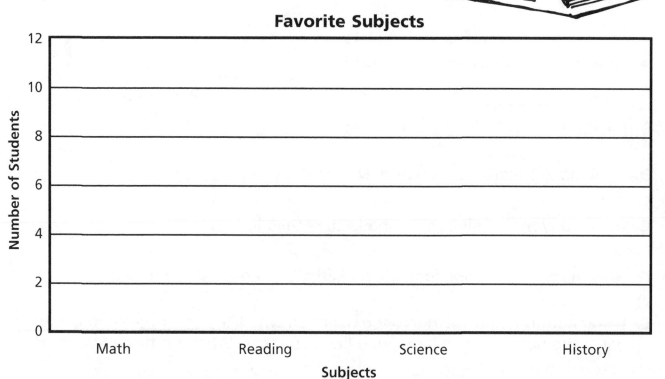

Favorite Subjects

Math Logic & Word Problems • 3–4 © 2005 Creative Teaching Press

Baby Elephant

SHOW ME THE WAY

The zoo proudly announced the arrival of baby Alyssa, a 250-pound African elephant, in June of last year. Every month Nikolai carefully weighed Alyssa and recorded the number on an index card along with other vital statistics. The cards were stored in a card file. When preparing for a first birthday celebration, Nikolai dropped the cards! Now they are out of order. Place the cards in order, and graph Alyssa's weight gain on a line graph.

March	1,125 lb.	February	1,000 lb.	January	925 lb.
June	250 lb.	April	1,250 lb.	August	425 lb.
October	675 lb.	December	850 lb.	November	750 lb.
July	350 lb.	May	1,300 lb.	September	550 lb.

Strategic Steps

1 Find June on the graph, and then go up to find 250 pounds and plot your point. Continue plotting the rest of the points.

2 The graph starts with June, the month of Alyssa's birth. Start at that point, and connect the points as her weight goes up.

Alyssa's Growth

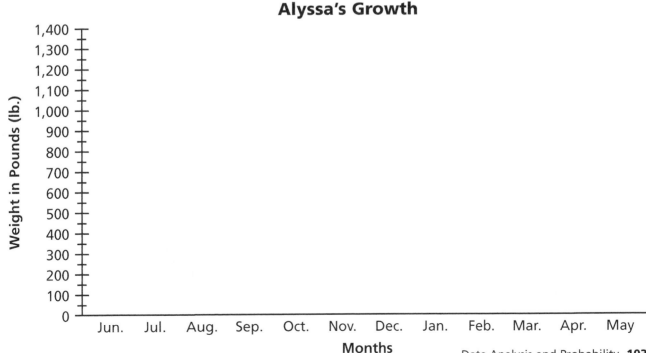

Carnival Activities

Lakeside Elementary School held a carnival last weekend, and now they are counting how many visitors played each game. To play a game, each person would pay with one ticket, so each ticket represents one person playing the game. The number of tickets was rounded to the nearest 5. Graph the results. Which game had the most players?

Game	Number of Tickets
Balloon Burst	125
Fishing	175
Cake Walk	250
Ring Toss	75
Dinosaur Dig	175
Dart Throw	225
Surprise Box	125
Duck Pond	100

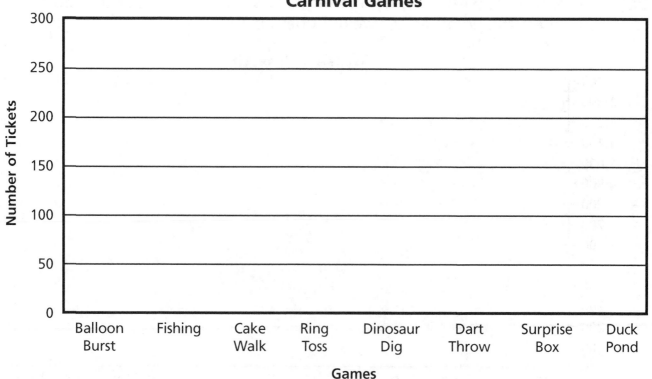

Math Logic & Word Problems • 3–4 © 2005 Creative Teaching Press

Pike's Peak

Ruthann and Roger were driving up Pike's Peak with their family and kept track of the animals they saw at different elevations. Now the children want to list the animals in order by their elevation. Ruthann and Roger have decided that a line graph is the easiest way to do this. Plot the animals and elevations on the graph.

- As they started the drive, they saw a deer at around 9,000 feet.
- At 10,500 feet, they saw a crow.
- From the summit at 14,100 feet, they saw an eagle soaring.
- One the way down the mountain, Roger saw a yellow-bellied marmot at 12,200 feet.
- Not long afterward, at 11,900 feet, Ruthann spied a bighorn sheep.
- When they stopped for a picnic lunch at 9,850 feet, they saw a ground squirrel.

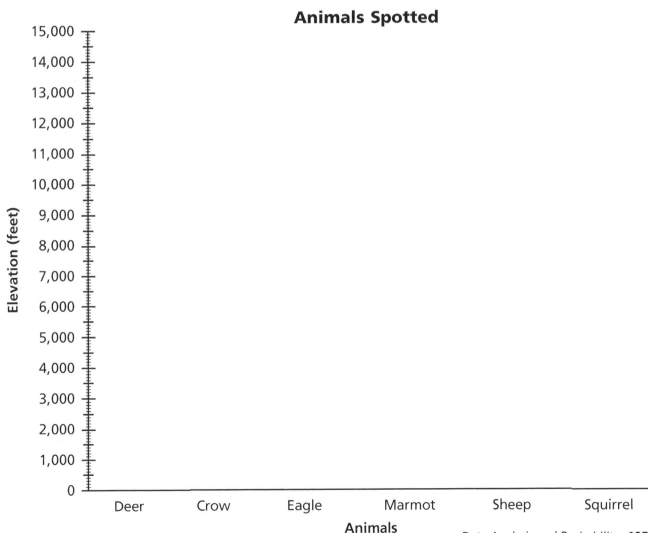

Animals Spotted

Baseball Tournament

SHOW ME THE WAY

There are eight baseball teams playing in a tournament.

- In the first round of the tournament, each team will play all the other teams. The four teams that win the most games will play in the second round.

- In the second round, each team will play one game. The winners of these games will play in the final round.

- The winner of the final round will win the tournament.

How many games will the winning team have played? _____

Strategic Steps

1 You need to draw a chart, as follows, to determine how many games are played in the first round.

Round One:

Team 1   Team 2
            Team 3
            Team 4
            Team 5
            Team 6
            Team 7
            Team 8

2 If you assume that Teams 1 through 4 won the most games, then the order of play in the second round is as follows:

Team 1   Team 2
Team 3   Team 4

3 If you assume that Team 1 and Team 4 won their games, then Team 1 will play against Team 4 in the third round.

4 To find the answer, count the number of games that Team 1 played.

Math Logic & Word Problems • 3–4 © 2005 Creative Teaching Press

Tennis Match

Ten players enter a tennis tournament. There will be three rounds.

- In the first round, each player will play all the other players. The four players who win the most matches will play in the second round.

- In the second round, each player will play one other player.

- In the third and final round, the two winners from the second round will play each other. The winner of this match is the winner of the tournament.

How many matches will the winner of the tournament have played? _____

First Round

Second Round

Final Round

All City Chess

Caroline entered the All City Chess tournament. There were a total of 12 players.

- For the first round, all twelve players played each of the other players. The six players who win the most games will play in the second round.

- In the second round, all six players will play each of the other players. The four players who win the most games will play in the semifinals.

- In the semifinals, each of the four players will play one game. The winners of these two games will play in the finals.

- Caroline played in the finals and won the game and the tournament.

How many total games of chess did she play? _____

First Round

Second Round

Third Round

Final Round

Math Logic & Word Problems • 3–4 © 2005 Creative Teaching Press

Bar Graphs

SHOW ME THE WAY

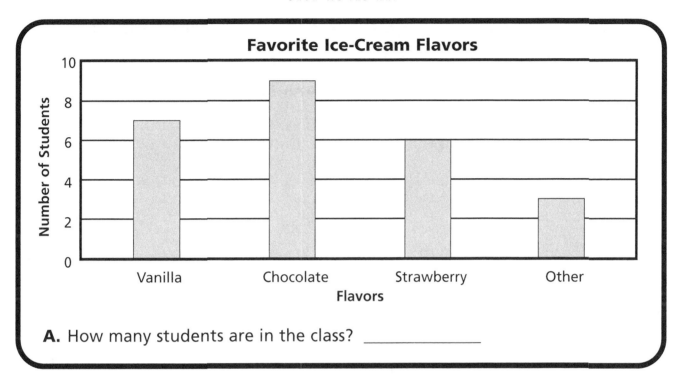

A. How many students are in the class? _____

Strategic Step

1 Add together the numbers from the ice-cream categories to find the total number of students.

B. How many more students like chocolate ice cream than like vanilla?

_____

Strategic Step

1 From the graph, find the number of children who like those flavors, and then write a number sentence.

_____

Name _____ Date _____

At the Zoo

Jessica and Tyler visited the zoo and saw many different animals. They drew this graph to compare the animals' weights.

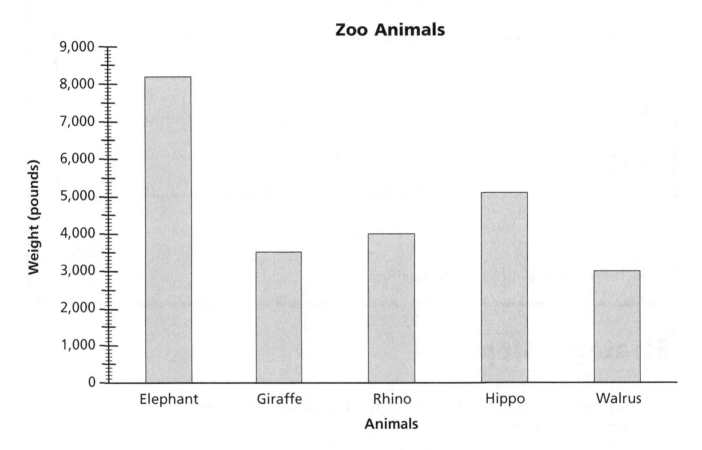

Use the bar graph to answer the questions.

A. Which animal weighs the most? _____

   How much does it weigh? _____

B. What is the difference in the weight of the largest and smallest animals?

   _____

C. Which two animals' weights can be added to equal almost that of the elephant?

   _____ and _____

Math Logic & Word Problems • 3–4 © 2005 Creative Teaching Press

Name _____ Date _____

Reading Contest

Jefferson Elementary School had a reading contest. The bar graph on the left shows the status halfway through the contest. The graph on the right shows the final results of the contest.

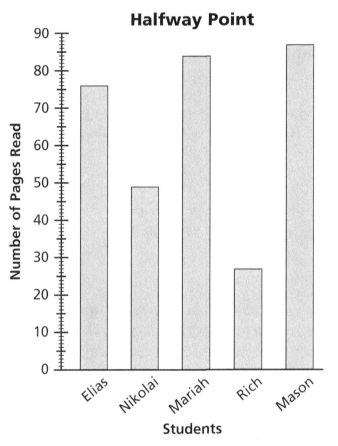

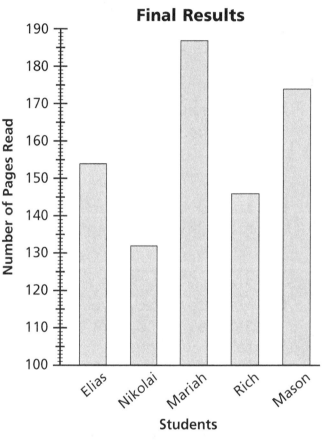

A. At the halfway point in the contest, who is leading? _____

By how much is that student ahead? _____

B. How many total pages have the students read so far? _____

C. How many pages did the winner read? _____

D. How many total pages did the students read? _____

How many more pages were read since the halfway point? _____

E. Which student read the most pages between the halfway point and the end of the contest?

_____

Math Logic & Word Problems • 3–4 © 2005 Creative Teaching Press

Name ______________________________ Date ______________

Probability

Show Me the Way

Probability is the likelihood or chance that something will happen. Probability can be written as a fraction, such as $\frac{1}{6}$, or as a ratio, such as 1:6. Both tell you that the chance of something happening is 1 in 6. When expressing probability as a fraction, remember to reduce the fraction to its lowest terms. For example, if the probability is $\frac{2}{6}$, you would reduce that to $\frac{1}{3}$.

A. You are playing a game that uses one die. You need to roll a 5 to win the game. What is the probability that you will roll a 5 with one roll?

____

B. In a deck of 26 alphabet cards, 5 cards are vowels. What is the probability of drawing a vowel card from this deck of cards?

____

C. There are six jackets in different colors in a closet. You are leaving for school early and want to reach in without turning on any lights. If you grab two jackets, what is the probability you will reach in and grab the blue jacket?

____

Strategic Steps

1. There are six numbers on each die. With any one roll, any number can turn up. So the probability of rolling any one number is $\frac{1}{6}$.

2. In question B, there are a total of 26 cards. Five of the cards are vowels. So the probability of drawing a vowel card is $\frac{5}{26}$.

3. In question C, there are a total of six possible outcomes. Since you are grabbing two jackets at once, that means your chance of getting the blue one is $\frac{2}{6}$. (Remember to reduce your fraction to $\frac{1}{3}$.)

Math Logic & Word Problems • 3–4 © 2005 Creative Teaching Press

What Are the Chances?

A. You are playing a game that has 5 dice. On your first throw, you roll four 3s. What is the probability that you will get a 3 on your next throw of the remaining die?

B. You have a bag that has 2 red, 3 blue, 1 white, and 4 green marbles. When you reach into the bag, what is the probability that you will pick out a blue marble?

C. You are caddying for your dad in the weekend golf game. You have a pouch with 4 blue, 6 red, 8 white, 3 pink, and 12 green golf tees. Your dad says that green golf tees are his favorite. If you reach into the pouch without looking, what is the probability that you will take out a green tee?

D. You have 4 red, 2 blue, 6 white, 3 black, and 2 green shirts in your drawer. If you reach in without looking, what is the probability that you will pick out a red shirt?

Math Logic & Word Problems • 3–4 © 2005 Creative Teaching Press

Take a Chance

A. Ray won a contest at a local radio station. He gets to reach into a bag with five slips of paper to find his prize. The prizes include a $100 gift certificate to a local video store, a video game, a new TV with a DVD, a new laptop computer, or the recent release of a video. He really wants a new laptop computer. What is the probability that he will draw that prize?

B. Your sister has a bag with 10 red, 12 yellow, 8 green, 14 pink, and 18 black jelly beans. You really like the red cinnamon-flavored jelly beans. What is the probability that you will pick one of those?

C. Clara has a box of buttons. She lost the white button from her blouse. In the button box, she has 22 white, 12 black, 8 red, and 30 blue buttons. What is the probability that she will pick out a white button on the first try?

D. Victor is getting dressed in the dark to avoid waking his younger brother. He has 18 pairs of socks in his drawer. There are 3 pairs of blue socks; ⅓ of the socks are black, and ½ are white. What is the probability that he will pick out a pair of white socks?

Math Logic & Word Problems • 3–4 © 2005 Creative Teaching Press

Favorite Colors

SHOW ME THE WAY

Ashley, Olivia, Nan, and Latasha are friends whose favorite colors are red, blue, green, and pink. Use the clues to match each girl with her favorite color.

- Olivia's favorite color does not have an "e" in it.
- Nan often compliments Ashley on her green sweater.
- Nan's favorite color does not have an "r" in it.
- Ashley never wears her favorite color.

	Red	Blue	Green	Pink
Olivia				
Nan				
Ashley				
Latasha				

Strategic Steps

1 Working with the first clue, it's easy to eliminate all the colors that have an "e." Next to Olivia's name, lightly put an "X" in each box of a color that can be eliminated. This will leave one color, pink. Write a large "Y" for "yes" in the pink box.

2 In the rows for the other girls, lightly put an "X" in the column under pink. Because that color has been assigned, the other girls cannot have that as a favorite color.

3 The second clue doesn't really help match either girl with a favorite color, so move on to the next clue. The third clue says that Nan's favorite color does not have an "r" in it. Mark out the colors with an "r," red and green, which leaves blue as Nan's favorite color. Once again, mark out blue as possibilities for the other girls.

4 The fourth clue says that Ashley never wears her favorite color. Go back to the second clue where we learned that Ashley often wears a green sweater. Use those two clues, and find Ashley's and Latasha's favorite colors.

Matching Clues

A. Christopher, Hunter, Jonas, and Caleb have birthdays in January, March, June, and August. Use the clues to match each boy to his birth month.

- Hunter and his friends went snowboarding on his last birthday.
- Jonas' birth month starts with the same letter as his name.
- Jonas usually has a pool party for his birthday.
- Christopher was born on the first day of spring.

	January	March	June	August
Christopher				
Hunter				
Jonas				
Caleb				

B. Julia, Kim, Dominic, and Joseph went to the zoo; and each had a favorite animal. Use the clues to match each child to his or her favorite animal.

- Dominic's favorite animal lives on an island and lives a very long time.
- Julia's favorite animal has only two legs.
- Joseph's favorite animal is larger than the others.

	Lion	Parrot	Galapagos Tortoise	Elephant
Julia				
Kim				
Dominic				
Joseph				

Math Logic & Word Problems • 3–4 © 2005 Creative Teaching Press

Solving Puzzles

A. Alan, Jerry, Dean, and Carol did reports on tyrannosaurus, stegosaurus, triceratops, and brontosaurus. Use the clues to match each child with his or her report.

- The name of Alan's dinosaur starts with a "T".
- Carol's dinosaur is the largest predator.
- Dean's report was on stegosaurus.

	Tyrannosaurus	Stegosaurus	Triceratops	Brontosaurus
Alan				
Jerry				
Dean				
Carol				

B. Leslie, Kevin, Doug, and Keisha all have different pets. One has a rabbit, one a gerbil, one a dog, and one a cat. Use the clues to match each child with the correct pet.

- The name of the rabbit's owner starts with a "K".
- Leslie usually hurries home to walk her pet.
- Keisha's pet has a wheel in its cage.
- Doug's pet purrs.

	Rabbit	Gerbil	Dog	Cat
Leslie				
Kevin				
Doug				
Keisha				

Which Bicycle?

Melanie, Leanne, Mark, and Susan all got new bicycles for Christmas. Each one has a different colored bicycle. The bicycles are yellow, red, white, and green. Use the clues to match each child with the correct bicycle.

- Melanie and the girl with the red bike live across the street from each other.

- Melanie's house, bike, notebook, and favorite T-shirt are all white.

- Melanie and Susan walk to school together since they live across the street from each other.

- Leanne bought a basket with yellow flowers to match her bicycle.

	Yellow	Red	White	Green
Melanie				
Leanne				
Mark				
Susan				

Math Logic & Word Problems • 3–4 © 2005 Creative Teaching Press

After School

Heather, Karen, Judy, Cheryl, and Stacey all signed up for after-school activities. The activities are woodworking, band, chess, reading, and drama. Use the clues to match each girl with her activity.

- Cheryl's activity requires a quiet room.

- Judy gave her dad a bird feeder that she made during her activity.

- Karen's activity has her playing a trombone.

- Heather goes to the library for her activity.

	Wood	Band	Chess	Reading	Drama
Heather					
Karen					
Judy					
Cheryl					
Stacey					

Volunteer Jobs

Curtis, Linda, Lin, Yonni, and Collin are all volunteering at the zoo this summer. Their jobs are selling tickets, cleaning cages, feeding animals, sweeping sidewalks, and selling snacks. Use the clues to match each child to the correct job.

- Collin wears old clothes so he won't get dirty on his job.

- Linda serves drinks as part of her job.

- Yonni has to remember which animal likes bananas.

- Lin has to be able to count money and make change for her job.

- Collin uses soap and water on his job.

	Selling Tickets	Cleaning Cages	Feeding Animals	Sweeping Sidewalks	Selling Snacks
Curtis					
Linda					
Lin					
Yonni					
Collin					

Math Logic & Word Problems • 3–4 © 2005 Creative Teaching Press

Lunch

Lynne, Daphne, Dustin, Daniel, and Elsa are having lunch together. They ordered a chicken-salad sandwich, a cheeseburger, a pepperoni pizza, tacos with cheese, and a spinach salad. Use the clues to match each child with the correct lunch.

- Dustin is a vegetarian.

- Lynne cannot eat cheese.

- Daniel does not like Italian or Mexican food.

- Daphne likes food with a soft bread crust.

	Chicken-Salad Sandwich	Cheeseburger	Pepperoni Pizza	Tacos	Spinach Salad
Lynne					
Daphne					
Dustin					
Daniel					
Elsa					

Answer Key

Jelly Beans (page 5)

27 jelly beans

The Penny Jar (page 6)

55 pennies

Marbles (page 7)

54 marbles

Who Is Older? (page 8)

Hannah	March	Mike	April
Rachel	February	Matthew	January
Emma	May		

Which Floor? (page 9)

Neha	5th floor	Will	3rd floor
Sarah	2nd floor	Katy	1st floor
Brodie	4th floor		

Classrooms (page 10)

Zane	Room 25	Danny	Room 23
Joey	Room 22	Cassandra	Room 21
Meagan	Room 24		

Backyard Leaves (page 11)

120 leaves

Yummy Muffins (page 12)

Mrs. Kim	8 muffins	Mr. Biggs	12 muffins
Miss Gardner	24 muffins	Mrs. Santos	12 muffins

How many muffins did Mr. Lang put out that morning?
60 muffins

Library Sale (page 13)

Nathaniel	40 books	Nellie	80 books
Delia	40 books	Edmund	40 books
Allison	20 books		

How many books did the five friends buy altogether?
220 books

Strawberry Field (page 14)

Jessica	4 plants	Brenna	6 plants
Kate	9 plants		

How many strawberry plants did they have left? 5 plants

Reading Contest (page 15)

Pete	16 pages	Betty	12 pages
Chalondra	16 pages	Margaret	20 pages

Runs (page 16)

Tim	6 runs	Decker	10 runs
Cody	12 runs	Dean	8 runs

What Operation? (page 17)

$6 + 7 = 13$ $(2 + 4) \times 6 = 36$

What Will You Do? (page 18)

A. $8 \times 4 = 32$ **B.** $42 = 7 \times 6$
C. $63 \div 7 = 9$ **D.** $32 - 21 = 11$
E. $6 \times 4 = 24$ **F.** $48 - 42 = 6$

G. $(24 - 14) + 18 = 28$ **H.** $(3 \times 7) - 6 = 15$
I. $(9 - 7) \times 12 = 24$ **J.** $(8 \times 3) - 4 = 20$
K. $(8 + 3) \times 3 = 33$ **L.** $36 = (4 - 2) \times 18$
M. $(4 \times 5) \times 2 = 40$ or $4 (5 \times 2)$ **N.** $(9 - 3) \times 3 = 18$

What Do You Pick? (page 19)

A. operation = subtraction; $18 - 7 = 11$
B. Did he gain or lose cards? gain; operation = subtraction;
$26 - 19 = 7$ more cards
C. operation = division; $48 \div 24 = 2$
D. yes; operation = multiplication;
$4 \times \$5 = \$20$ per bushel, $12 \times 20 = \$240$

Place Value Riddles (page 20)

A. 3005   **C.** 5068
B. 4032

Where Do I Go? (page 21)

A. 3,420   **C.** 8,153
B. 8,008   **D.** 49,473

Riddle Contest (page 22)

A. 852,264   **D.** 8,035
B. 4,235,670   **E.** Answers will vary.
C. 943

What Do I Need? (page 23)

A. 225 acorns   **B.** not enough information

Too Much or Too Little? (page 24)

A. not enough information; we don't know the cost
of popcorn
B. 15 peaches
C. not enough information; we don't know how many
brothers Martina has
D. 1 cup dry ingredients
E. $7.35

What Do I Really Need? (page 25)

A. too much information; 4:30 p.m.

B. too much information; 160 square inches

C. not enough information; we don't know how many miles he rode those days

D. right amount of information; 288

E. too much information; 1 minute, 20 seconds

Fractions (page 26)

A. 3 ducks

B. same size

C. $\frac{1}{10}$, $\frac{1}{4}$, $\frac{1}{3}$, $\frac{1}{2}$

What Part? (page 27)

A. 2

B. they received the same amount

C. $\frac{1}{2}$, $\frac{1}{3}$, $\frac{1}{4}$, $\frac{1}{8}$

D. $\frac{2}{3}$ cup

Who Has More? (page 28)

A. 3

B. Brad had more.

C. $\frac{1}{8}$, $\frac{1}{4}$, $\frac{1}{2}$, $\frac{2}{3}$

D. $\frac{5}{8}$

How Many Steps? (page 29)

A. 8 cookies per plate

B. 262 cards

More Than One Step (page 30)

A. $36.50

B. 65,000 balloons

C. 2 trucks; 2,160 balls in each truck

D. 3 slices of pizza

First This, Then That (page 31)

A. 46 comic books

B. 25 cents

C. 240 passes

D. 3 cars

Can You Guess? (page 32)

A. 3 quarters, 1 dime, 1 nickel, and 2 pennies

B. 12 and 14

Your Guess, Please (page 33)

A. 6 bison and 6 cranes

B. blouse and T-shirt

C. 18 and 6

D. corn and watermelon

Can You Double-Check That? (page 34)

A. 4 dogs; 5 birds

B. 1 quarter, 1 dime, 1 nickel, and 3 pennies

C. 9 and 16

D. a game and an action figure

Riddle Me a Number (page 35)

A. 28

B. 15

And the Answer Is... (page 36)

A. 27

B. 43

C. 8

D. 71

Solve Our Riddles (page 37)

A. 71

B. 168

C. 36

D. 96

The Toy Store (page 38)

A. $2.33

B. 25 weeks

Allowances (page 39)

A. 25 cents

B. $5.07

C. $4.00

D. 7 weeks since he needs $14.25 more

E. She will have $2.50 left for ice cream.

The Carnival (page 40)

A. $14.00

B. 40 tickets; 10 tickets each

C. $40.00

D. 45 tickets for $9

E. $480.00

What Time Will It Be? (page 41)

A. 2 hours, 45 minutes

B. 6:00 p.m.

In a Hurry? (page 42)

A. 4:30; 5:15

B. yes

C. 11:15 a.m.

D. 2 hours, 30 minutes

Is It Time Yet? (page 43)

A. 4:00 p.m.

B. 45 minutes

C. 3:45 p.m.

D. 2 hours, 15 minutes

Let's Double (page 44)

Year	Blooms	Year	Blooms
1	1	6	32
2	2	7	64
3	4	8	128
4	8	9	256
5	16	10	512

Science Experiment (page 45)

10 generations: 512   20 generations: 524,288

Charlotte's Decision (page 46)

Charlotte should choose the penny doubled every day for 10 days. A penny doubled every day for 10 days would give her $10.24.

Day 1	$0.02	Day 6	$0.64
Day 2	$0.04	Day 7	$1.28
Day 3	$0.08	Day 8	$2.56
Day 4	$0.16	Day 9	$5.12
Day 5	$0.32	Day 10	$10.24

Decimals (page 47)

A. 0.5 left to mow   B. Madison, Wesley, Kathy, Lara, Aaron

More Decimals (page 48)

A. 0.3 of the bag   C. 5.2 bottles of drink
B. 2.3 packs of paper   D. 0.5 acre, 1.3 acres, 1.7 acres, 1.75 acres, 2.3 acres

Cameron's Day (page 49)

A. 0.8 cup   C. deer, beaver, buffalo, alligator, fox
B. 0.4 of the chapter   D. 9.3 feet

The Hardware Store (page 50)

A. 7 boards   C. 5 boards
B. 13 pounds   D. 5 packages of nuts and bolts

The Family Reunion (page 51)

A. 4 packages of hot dogs   D. 6 pies
B. 5 packages of buns   E. 3 packages of plates, tableware, and cups
C. 5 containers of potato salad

The Party (page 52)

A. 24 servings   C. 2 packages of treat bags
B. 20 bags of balloons   D. 4 packages of yo-yos

Guess the Ages (page 53)

A. Wayne   10   Judy   6

All in the Family (page 54)

A. David	13	C. Lisa	16
Mia	8	Laura	13
B. Jose and Milo	2	D. Cole's dad	32
		Cole's grandfather	64

How Old? (page 55)

A. Timothy	21	C. aunt	18
Amanda	16	Shi Ann	12
		cousin	6
B. Manuel	14	D. Leroy	11
uncle	28	brother	3

What Is Missing? (page 56)

A. 6   C. 12   E. 6
B. 12   D. 168; 9   F. 26

Missing Numbers (page 57)

A. 5   C. 6   E. 7
B. 24   D. 3; 22   F. 33

Something Is Missing (page 58)

A. 9   C. 48   E. 6
B. 33   D. 68; 6   3; 27   F. 168

Magic Squares (page 59)

4	9	2
3	5	7
8	1	6

Is It Magic? (page 60)

9	1	8
5	6	7
4	11	3

10	5	6
3	7	11
8	9	4

Fill in the Blanks (page 61)

7	2	3
0	4	8
5	6	1

11	34	24
36	23	10
22	12	35

16	3	2	13
5	10	11	8
9	6	7	12
4	15	14	1

Patterns (page 62)

A. 10, 12, 14

B. △, □, ○   C. □, 3, △

Find the Pattern (page 63)

A. 32, 64, 128   D. $\frac{1}{6}$, $\frac{1}{7}$, $\frac{1}{8}$
B. 6, 4, 2   E. 54, 65, 76
C. □, △, ○

More Patterns (page 64)

A. **2**, 4, 6, **8**, 10, **12**

B. trapezoid, circle, square, triangle, trapezoid, circle, square, triangle

C. ½, ⅙, ⅕, ¼, ⅓, ½

D. triangle, square, square, triangle, square, square, triangle, square

E. 1, 1, 2, 3, 5, **8**, 13, **21**, 34 (adding the 2 numbers before it)

Guess My Number (page 65)

6

What Number Am I? (page 66)

A. 4   B. 17

Find a Number (page 67)

A. 4   B. 14

Area Puzzles (page 68)

A. 154 square feet

B. The area of the pool is 120 square feet and larger than the space, so his parents did not buy it.

What Is the Area? (page 69)

A. front yard = 900 square meters
backyard = 1,125 square meters
The backyard is 225 square meters larger.

B. 56 square inches

C. 21 bags of concrete

Assignment Area (page 70)

A. notebook paper: 156 square inches
teacher's desk: 20 square feet
bulletin board: 8 square feet

B. notebook paper, bulletin board, teacher's desk

C. floor = 80 square feet; they need 80 tiles

Perimeter in the Home (page 71)

A. 60 centimeters

B. No, the perimeter of the cake is 46 inches.

Perimeter Puzzlers (page 72)

A. 48 feet   C. 42 meters

B. 12 meters

Mr. Dennis's Assignment (page 73)

A. 48 inches   C. 40 feet

B. 23 centimeters   D. 66 feet

Which Do I Choose? (page 74)

A. $60 + 40 + 60 + 40 = 200$ feet of fence

B. $3 \times 5 = 15$ bags of soil

School Play (page 75)

A. perimeter; $24 + 18 + 24 + 18 = 84$ feet of rod

B. area; $2 \times 3 = 6$ square feet

C. perimeter; $6 + 3 + 6 + 3 = 18$ feet

D. area; $8 \times 6 = 48$ square feet

Area or Perimeter? (page 76)

A. perimeter; $12 + 9 + 12 + 9 = 42$ feet

B. area; $12 \times 9 = 108$ square feet; 108 bags of soil

C. area; $12 \times 9 = 108$ square feet

Congruency (page 77)

A. not congruent   C. not congruent

B. congruent

Pottery (page 78)

A. Answers will vary.   C. Answers will vary.

B. Answers will vary.

Congruent or Not? (page 79)

A. yes, because they are the same shape and all their sides are the same lengths

B. no, because they have different lengths and number of sides

C.

D. Answers will vary.

Shape Puzzles (page 80)

A. square   C. circle

B. right triangle   D. rectangle

Quadrilaterals, Triangles, and Circles, Oh My! (page 81)

A. parallelogram   C. octagon

B. pentagon   D. trapezoid

Riddle Me This (page 82)

A. rhombus   C. hexagon

B. rectangle or square   D. oval

Measure Up (page 83)

A. 12 ounces

B. She needs 88 inches and has 56 inches left over.

How Much? (page 84)

A. 3 cups

B. 8 ounces

C. Yes. There are 16 cups in a gallon, and he uses 11 cups.

Math All Around Us (page 85)

A. 36 inches; 3 feet

B. 71 square meters

C. 20 laps

Changing Units (page 86)

A. 3,520 yards

B. 5,400 inches

How Many? (page 87)

A. 3,600 inches

B. 3.2 kilometers

C. 24 bows

D. 500 meters

The Hiking Trip (page 88)

A. She can take the booklet about wildflowers.

B. Answers will vary. Accept any items with a total weight that is less than 5 kilograms.

Baking Cookies (page 89)

A. 2 cups butter
   4 cups sugar
   4 eggs
   6 cups flour
   2 cups walnuts
   2 cups chocolate chips

B. 4 cups butter
   8 cups sugar
   8 eggs
   12 cups flour
   4 cups walnuts
   4 cups chocolate chips

Birthday Party (page 90)

A. 27 lemons
   36 cups water
   4 ½ cups sugar

B. 1 ½ cups unsweetened cocoa powder
   3 cups flour
   3 teaspoons baking powder
   1 ½ teaspoons salt
   1 ½ cups butter
   6 eggs
   4 ½ cups sugar

Pizza Fun (page 91)

Pizza Dough (makes 5 pizzas)
4 ½ cups warm water
5 tablespoons active yeast
5 teaspoons sugar
2 ½ teaspoons salt
10 tablespoons oil
12 ½ cups flour

Sauce (for 5 pizzas)
2 medium tomatoes
1 onion
1 teaspoon sugar
2 teaspoons fresh basil
3 cloves garlic

How Much Do I Need? (page 92)

12-ounce bag

Now You're Cooking (page 93)

A. eight 8-ounce bags, or four 16-ounce bags, or three 16-ounce bags and two 8-ounce bags

B. 500 milliliters and 450 milliliters

C. six 8-ounce bags or twelve 4-ounce bags

D. five 2-liter bottles

Construction Woes (page 94)

Answers will vary. Possible answers include:

A. centimeters

B. gallons

C. foot

D. centimeters

E. inches

F. gallon, gallon

G. gallons

H. inches

I. gallons

Cooking School (page 95)

1 inch (cup)

½ mile (teaspoon)

1 meter (teaspoon)

1 yard (cup)

¼ gallon (cup)

1 kilometer (tablespoons)

1 yard (cup)

1 liter (tablespoon)

2 pounds (cups)

1 centimeter (cup)

2 feet (cups)

Wild West Adventures (page 96)

30-centimeter (feet)

20 gallons (meters)

10-yard (gallon)

½ pint (kilometer)

12 inches (miles)

20-mile (ounce)

2 acres (pounds)

Ice-Cream Toppings (page 97)

6 different combinations

Your Order, Please (page 98)

10 different combinations

Cheese: mushrooms
         peppers
         onions
         tomatoes

Mushrooms: peppers
            onions
            tomatoes

Peppers: onions
          tomatoes

Onions: tomatoes

Tomatoes: no new mixtures

School Colors (page 99)

21 different combinations; with 22 students there will be one repeated combination

Red: blue
yellow
green
black
white
purple

Blue: yellow
green
black
white
purple

Yellow: green
black
white
purple

Green: black
white
purple

Black: white
purple

White: purple

Purple: no new combinations

Camp Activities (page 100)

A. 20
B. 2
C. hiking

Sports (page 101)

A. Football   10   Soccer   5   Basketball   8
   Baseball   3   Hockey   4
B. 30
C. 4
D. 21
E. soccer and baseball

Favorite Subject (page 102)

A. Math   6   Reading   10
   Science   4   History   2

B.

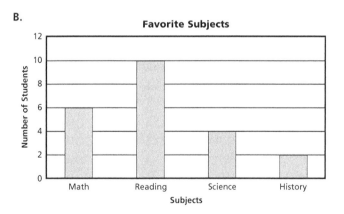

Baby Elephant (page 103)

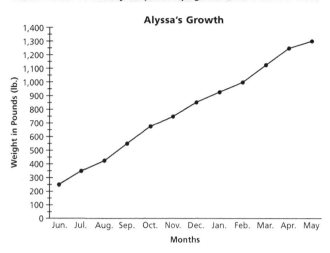

Carnival Activities (page 104)

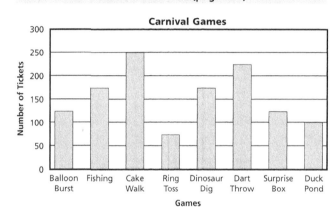

Pike's Peak (page 105)

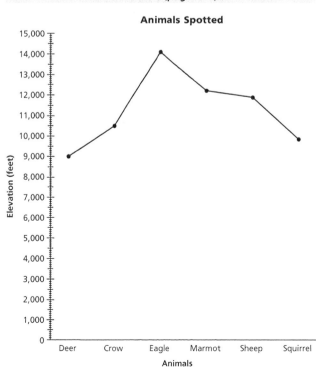

Baseball Tournament (page 106)

The winning team will have played 9 games.

Tennis Match (page 107)

The winner will have played 11 matches.

All City Chess (page 108)

Caroline played 18 games.

Bar Graphs (page 109)

A. 25 students
B. $9 - 7 = 2$ children

At the Zoo (page 110)

A. elephant; 8,200 pounds
B. 5,200 pounds
C. hippo and walrus

Reading Contest (page 111)

A. Mason; 3 pages ahead of next student
B. 323 pages
C. 187 pages
D. 793 pages; 470 pages
E. Rich

Probability (page 112)

A. $\frac{1}{6}$
B. $\frac{5}{26}$
C. $\frac{2}{6}$ or $\frac{1}{3}$

What Are the Chances? (page 113)

A. $\frac{1}{6}$
B. $\frac{3}{10}$
C. $\frac{12}{33}$
D. $\frac{6}{17}$

Take a Chance (page 114)

A. $\frac{1}{5}$
B. $\frac{10}{62}$ or $\frac{5}{31}$
C. $\frac{22}{72}$ or $\frac{11}{36}$
D. $\frac{1}{2}$

Favorite Colors (page 115)

Ashley	red
Nan	blue
Olivia	pink
Latasha	green

Matching Clues (page 116)

A.
Christopher	March
Hunter	January
Jonas	June
Caleb	August

B.
Julia	parrot
Kim	lion
Dominic	Galapagos tortoise
Joseph	elephant

Solving Puzzles (page 117)

A.
Alan	triceratops
Jerry	brontosaurus
Dean	stegosaurus
Carol	tyrannosaurus

B.
Leslie	dog
Kevin	rabbit
Doug	cat
Keisha	gerbil

Which Bicycle? (page 118)

Melanie	white
Leanne	yellow
Mark	green
Susan	red

After School (page 119)

Heather	reading
Karen	band
Judy	woodworking
Cheryl	chess
Stacey	drama

Volunteer Jobs (page 120)

Curtis	sweeping sidewalks
Linda	selling snacks
Lin	selling tickets
Yonni	feeding animals
Collin	cleaning cages

Lunch (page 121)

Lynne	chicken-salad sandwich
Daphne	pepperoni pizza
Dustin	spinach salad
Daniel	cheeseburger
Elsa	tacos